FOOD HYGIENE AND SAFETY

A HANDBOOK FOR CARE PRACTITIONERS

Carolyn Meggitt

Heinemann
Inspiring generations

Heinemann Educational Publishers
Halley Court, Jordan Hill, Oxford OX2 8EJ
Part of Harcourt Education

Heinemann is the registered trademark of
Harcourt Education Limited

First published 2003

08 07 06 05 04 03
10 9 8 7 6 5 4 3 2 1

British Library Cataloguing in Publication Data is available
from the British Library on request.

ISBN 0 435 45531 1

Typeset by Saxon Graphics Ltd, Derby
Printed in the UK by Bath Press Ltd

Acknowledgements
The author and publisher would like to thank the following individuals and organisations for permission to reproduce photographs:

Alamy page 126; Corbis/Bob Rowan page 7; FLPA/Terry Whittaker page 148; Sally & Richard Greenhill/Sally Greenhill pages 4, 78 and 170; Holt Studios page 145; Carolyn Meggit page 111; Peter Morris pages 87–9, 97, 105 and 135; Science Photo Library/Antonia Reeve page 169; Science Photo Library/CC Studio page 117; Science Photo Library/Dr. Jeremy Burgess pages 140–1; Science Photo Library/Gusto page 143; Science Photo Library/Peter Scoones page146; Gerald Sunderland page 110.

Crown copyright material on page 10 is reproduced under Class license number C01W0000141 with the permission of the Controller of HSMO and the Queen's Printer for Scotland.

Every effort has been made to contact copyright holders of material reproduced in this book. Any omissions will be rectified in subsequent printings if notice is given to the publishers.

Tel: 01865 888058 www.heinemann.co.uk

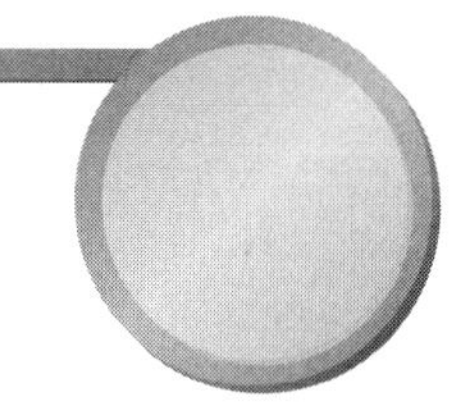

Contents

Introduction

Who this book is for

This book gives clear guidelines on food handling for anyone working as a care practitioner. You could be:

- **a care worker in a residential or nursing home for elderly clients**
- **an early years worker (or nursery nurse) in a day nursery, school or special school**
- **an auxiliary or nursing aide in a hospital**
- **a home care assistant caring for clients in their own homes**
- **a playgroup leader**
- **a school lunch supervisor.**

Whatever your role, your work is likely to involve preparing or serving food to clients – and you will need to be able to do this safely and hygienically.

How this book can help you

Food hygiene is a mandatory part of most courses leading to a qualification in care work. The information in this book will help you to understand:

- the importance of food hygiene
- how food poisoning occurs
- what to do when preparing and serving food
- what problems may occur and how to deal with them
- your responsibilities to your clients and your employers
- the laws relating to food hygiene.

How the book is structured

Part 1 looks at the principles of food hygiene – what is food hygiene and how poor food and personal hygiene can lead to food poisoning.

Part 2 explains how you can act to prevent food poisoning at each stage of the food handling process – from storage of food and its preparation, to cooking and serving, to the cleaning of food areas and equipment, disposal of waste and the control of pests. Finally, it covers the main laws and regulations on food hygiene and safety – you will need to be aware of these as you carry out food handling duties.

Throughout the book there are:

- Keys to Good Practice, which provide guidelines to best practice in food handling
- interesting Quick Facts
- Case Studies based on real-life scenarios
- Safety Tips
- Knowledge Tests at the end of every chapter – answers are provided on pages 177–181.

The Glossary on pages 173–175 will help you to check your understanding of the terms used in food hygiene and safety.

Part 1

The principles of food hygiene

Chapter 1

The importance of food hygiene

Food hygiene refers to the practices which should be followed to make sure that food is safe and wholesome throughout all the stages of production from purchase to consumption (eating).

Whenever you handle food you need to be aware of food hygiene. That means you should know how to store and prepare food correctly. Poor food hygiene can lead to food poisoning, and in the caring environment in particular, food poisoning can be extremely dangerous.

This chapter looks at why food hygiene is essential, what food poisoning is and who is most likely to be at risk from its effects. It covers the following topics:

- ❑ **Why is food hygiene essential?**
- ❑ **What is food poisoning?**
- ❑ **What causes food poisoning?**
- ❑ **Who can get food poisoning?**
- ❑ **The impact of food poisoning.**
- ❑ **Why has there been an increase in food poisoning?**
- ❑ **Good working practices.**

Why is food hygiene essential?

Food hygiene is essential because the food we eat plays an important part in keeping us healthy. Food hygiene involves more than cleanliness. To help keep food safe and hygienic, you will need to:

- ➤ protect it from the risk of contamination by harmful **bacteria** (germs), poisons, chemicals and foreign bodies – that is, anything which should *not* be present in the food such as insects, a plaster from a food handler's finger, fragments of glass or china, jewellery, hair and staples from food packaging

- prevent germs from multiplying to the point where the food is a risk to health
- destroy any harmful bacteria already in the food by thorough cooking at the correct temperature
- throw away unfit or **contaminated** food.

When working in the caring sector you will almost always be involved in handling food in some way. For example, you might:

- prepare and serve snacks or meals for children in a nursery
- serve meals to patients in a hospital or a day unit
- serve meals to clients in a residential home
- supervise meal-times in a school.

You have a responsibility to learn how to keep the food you handle safe and hygienic, because the people you care for are dependent on you. They need you to provide them with nourishing food which is safe for them to eat, and which will not make them ill with **food poisoning**.

Serving food

What is food poisoning?

Any infectious disease or unpleasant illness which results from consuming contaminated food or drink is known as **food poisoning**. The term is most often used to describe an acute illness, often with symptoms such as diarrhoea and/or vomiting.

Ten children treated after E. coli outbreak in nursery

Ten toddlers and a parent are being treated for serious food poisoning after an outbreak of the most virulent form of E. coli at a private nursery in the Yorkshire Dales.

Four of the children, aged between one and four, are in hospitals, one of them with a kidney condition, haemolytic uraemic syndrome, which is triggered by the stomach bug.

The nursery has been closed while tests try to trace the cause of the outbreak, which has been confirmed as E. coli 0157, the most severe strain of the bug. Dr Ebere Okereke, North Yorkshire's consultant for communicable disease control, said the closure was a precaution. 'It does not mean that there is anything wrong with the nursery. It's to prevent the young children, who are not good at washing their hands, spreading it to one another.'

Laboratory tests may reveal further cases of the disease, which has a nine-day incubation. Symptoms include severe vomiting, diarrhoea, fever and passing blood.

Source: Guardian, 30 November 2002

Food poisoning can happen all too easily and is extremely dangerous, particularly to people who are frail or already unwell.

What causes food poisoning?

Food poisoning is sickness caused by:

- bacteria or **viruses** in food
- **moulds** which cause toxins (poisons), for example on nuts
- eating some poisonous plants, for example toadstools, under-cooked red kidney beans
- eating poisonous fish or shellfish such as the Japanese puffer fish

- chemicals in food, for example cleaning agents and insecticides when used incorrectly may get into the food.

Although food intolerances and allergic reactions to certain foods may result in a similar sudden illness, they are *not* food poisoning as they are not caused by the food being contaminated by harmful bacteria, chemicals or viruses. Most cases of food poisoning result from eating **pathogenic** (or harmful) **bacteria** which are living on the food. Nearly all food poisoning is preventable although it is not possible to completely eliminate the risk.

For more information on food poisoning, see Chapter 3, pages 26–46.

Below are nine ways in which people (including you!) can get food poisoning:

Nine main reasons for food poisoning outbreaks

1. Food which is not kept at the right temperature, for example food that is prepared in advance and left at room temperature instead of being refrigerated. This will cause food poisoning bacteria to multiply.
2. Cooling food too slowly before refrigeration. While the food is still warm, the bacteria multiply.
3. Not reheating ready-to-eat food to high enough temperatures to destroy food poisoning bacteria.
4. Using cooked food contaminated with food poisoning bacteria.
5. Not cooking to a high enough temperature or for the correct length of time.
6. Not thawing frozen poultry correctly.
7. **Cross-contamination** from raw food to a high risk food, for example when the juices from uncooked meat drip on to a fruit mousse.
8. Eating raw food, such as eggs, shellfish or milk, which may already be contaminated.
9. Infected food handlers, which includes people who are currently suffering from or have recently had a **food-borne illness** or any illness with similar symptoms.

Who can get food poisoning?

Anyone can get food poisoning, but for some people food poisoning can be especially dangerous. The following groups of people are often more likely to experience food poisoning and are less able to fight off the infection:

- babies and young children
- elderly people
- pregnant women
- people who are already ill.

Babies and young children

Babies and very young children are at particular risk from food poisoning partly because they have immature immune systems and so are unable to fight off the infection when it gets into their bodies. Also, infection can spread very quickly in groups of young children if there is a lack of supervised thorough hand washing after using the toilet and before eating, and from touching contaminated toilet seats and tap handles. Many young children also tend to put their hands, fingers and thumbs in their mouths frequently, so infection can be passed from the hands into the mouth and rest of the body.

Elderly people

Elderly people are at particular risk because as we age:

- our immune systems weaken
- stomach acid also decreases – and stomach acid plays an important role in reducing the number of bacteria in our gut
- there is an increased likelihood of underlying problems – for example, illnesses such as diabetes, some cancer treatments and kidney disease may increase a person's risk of getting food poisoning.

Pregnant women

The most likely risk to both the mother's and her baby's health during pregnancy is listeriosis. The cause is the bacterium Listeria which can be found in soft cheeses and pre-cooked foods (see also Chapter 3, page 42). Although it usually only causes mild food poisoning in adults, listeriosis is a serious infection to catch in pregnancy. It can cause stillbirth, premature labour and miscarriage. There can also be serious consequences if the baby has to be delivered early. The baby may be very ill and need antibiotics to prevent complications like meningitis and poisoning of the blood (septicaemia).

People who are already ill

People who suffer from long-term illness may have reduced immunity (**immunodeficiency**), and certain treatments for their illness cause their immune systems to be suppressed (**immuno-suppression**). As a result, they will be unable to fight off infections and so they will be at greater risk from all types of food poisoning.

- Many cancers can cause immunodeficiency.
- Immuno-suppression is a common side-effect of chemotherapy used to treat many types of cancer because the chemotherapy often reduces the number of white blood cells available to fight infection.

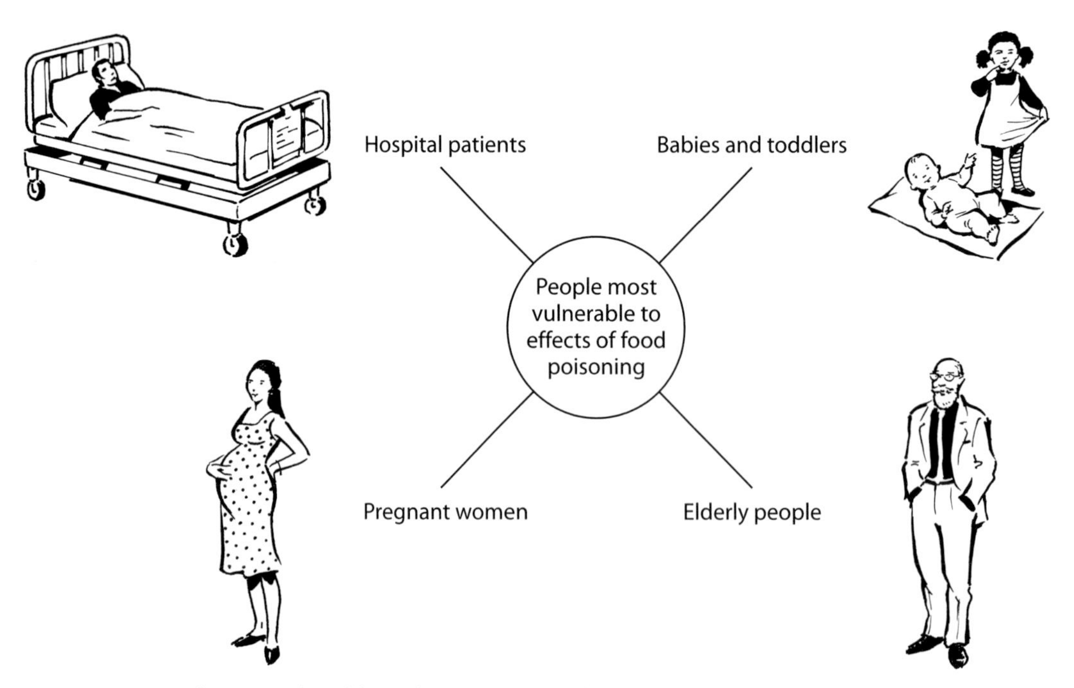

People most vulnerable to the effects of food poisoning

- Acquired immunodeficiency may be a complication of diseases such as HIV infection and AIDS (Acquired Immunodeficiency Syndrome).
- Malnutrition, particularly with lack of protein, can cause acquired immunodeficiency.

People who regularly take antacids, a drug which reduces the amount of acid in the stomach, are also vulnerable to food poisoning. This is because the food poisoning bacteria prefer an alkaline rather than an acid environment.

You have a serious responsibility to those you care for to make sure that the food you prepare and handle is safe – that it does not cause illness, injury or any other health problem. (There are also legal obligations for ensuring that the food you handle is safe to eat – see Chapter 11, pages 152–172).

The impact of food poisoning

Food poisoning can make you feel anything from being slightly off-colour to being so ill that you need medical attention. The **Food Standards Agency** estimates that up to 4.5 million people in the UK suffer from food poisoning each year. While many of these cases will be fairly mild, a significant number result in serious illness or even death.

The number of *reported* and then hospitalised cases of **food-borne illness** (illness that is spread by food and water) is increasing and there are many more cases which go unreported. The number of cases of food poisoning notified in the UK since 1985 is shown in the graph on page 10.

Number of notified cases of food poisoning (UK)
Source: Office of Population Censuses and Surveys, Scottish Centre for Infection and Environmental Health and Regional Information Branch, Department of Health and Social Security, Belfast

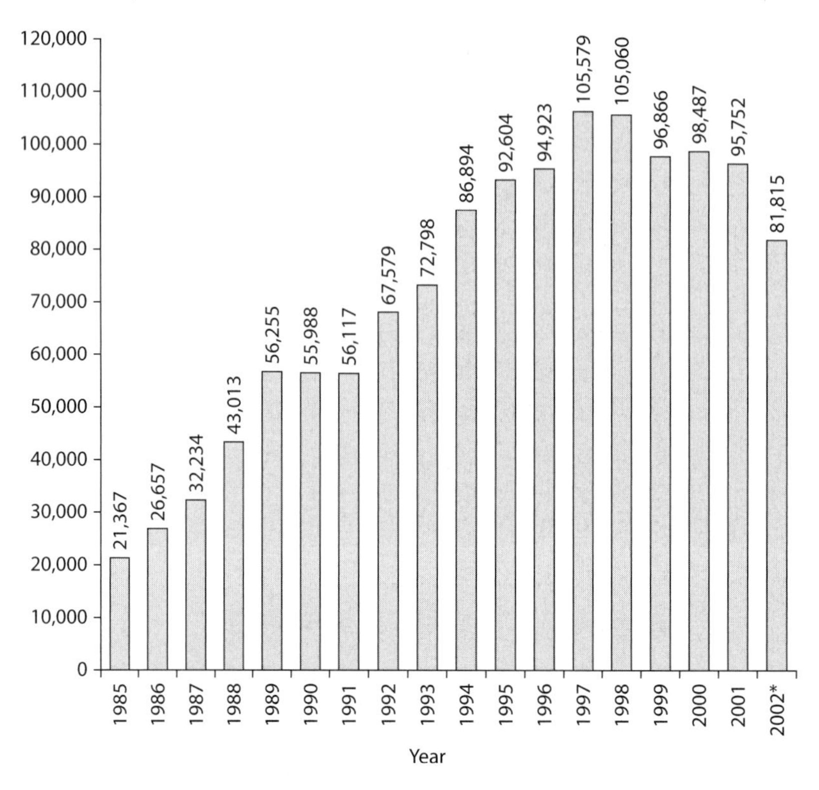

Cases of food poisoning notified in the UK since 1985 (* denotes provisional figure)

Why has there been an increase in food poisoning?

The number of reported cases of food poisoning is increasing. There are several reasons for this, including:

- changes in public awareness – a greater awareness of food poisoning means more cases are reported
- changes in lifestyle – an increased reliance on convenience foods and ready-to-eat meals which only need heating up; more snacks and meals being eaten away from home; the trend for outdoor eating such as barbecues and picnics

- changes in shopping habits – shopping weekly, buying in bulk and storing food at home for longer periods
- better public awareness – more attention is given to food hygiene issues in the media
- changes in recording statistics – a wider range of illnesses is now included in the official figures, for example some bacteria have only recently become recognised as causes of food poisoning.

To prevent food poisoning, everyone involved in food production – 'from the farm to the fork' – must have high standards of food safety and hygiene. Along the food chain, each person is responsible for protecting the food, for example through:

- checking hygiene
- making sure food is stored at the correct temperature
- ensuring clean storage
- preventing contamination
- correct preparation and cooking.

Good working practices

When you handle food as part of your job, you are responsible for ensuring that food does not become *contaminated*. You need to understand how current legislation affects your work and to follow good working practices. These practices are described in detail throughout this book, but in general include the ones shown on page 12.

Keys to Good Practice

- ✔ Keep yourself clean by following rules of personal hygiene.
- ✔ Know how to store and prepare food safely and hygienically.
- ✔ Ensure that areas for serving food are clean and safe.
- ✔ Protect food from anything which could cause harm.
- ✔ Be alert to food safety **hazards** and take action to ensure that they do not cause harm.
- ✔ Ensure clients are given the opportunity to wash their hands before a meal.

Activity: Lifestyle changes and food poisoning

1 Using the following headings, explain how changes in lifestyle and eating habits may have led to a rise in the number of cases of food poisoning:

  a Changes in shopping habits – for example widespread use of supermarkets.

  b Lifestyle changes – for example more eating take-away foods or outdoor eating.

  c The use of ready-prepared meals which only require reheating in a microwave or oven.

2 Give reasons why it is likely that only one in every 50 cases of food poisoning is reported.

Knowledge Test

1 Which groups of people are likely to be seriously affected by food poisoning, and why?

2 Why are people who regularly take antacids more vulnerable to food poisoning?

(Answers on page 177.)

Chapter 2

Microbiology

In order to understand how food poisoning happens, and therefore how to prevent it, you will need to learn about the living organisms which cause food poisoning. These organisms are called micro-organisms because they are so small. Given the right temperature and conditions, they will grow and multiply until they can be extremely dangerous. The study of the life of these micro-organisms is called microbiology.

This chapter looks at the microbiology of food poisoning organisms. It covers the following topics:

- ❑ **What are bacteria?**
- ❑ **Helpful and harmful bacteria (pathogens).**
- ❑ **How bacteria multiply.**
- ❑ **Spores, toxins and viruses.**
- ❑ **Moulds and yeasts.**
- ❑ **Spoilage organisms (the organisms which damage food).**

What are bacteria?

Bacteria (often called germs) are single-celled micro-organisms which are too small to be seen without the use of a very powerful microscope. They are everywhere – in the water and soil and inside other living organisms, including animals and human beings.

Examples of diseases caused by bacteria include:

- sore throat (streptococcal infection)
- pneumonia
- boils and abscesses (staphylococcus infection)
- food poisoning, for example salmonella (see pages 32–6) and staphylococcus aureus (see page 36)
- tetanus
- cholera

- some sexually transmitted diseases.

You can pick up bacterial diseases from:

- infected animals and rodents

- infected human beings

- insects

- contaminated objects

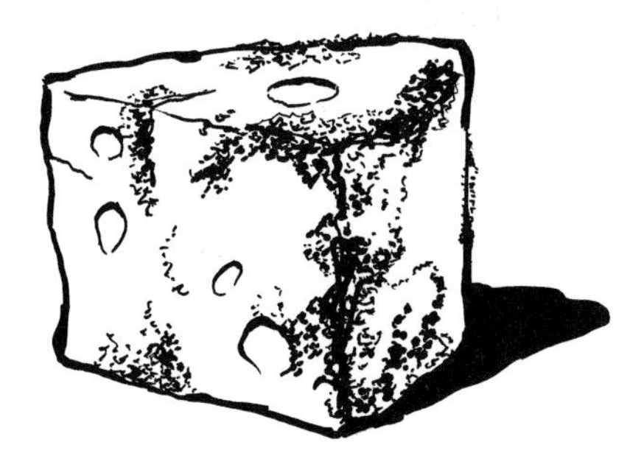

- contaminated food or water.

Quick facts

- Bacteria are everywhere.
- Most bacteria are not harmful, for example, some are used to make cheese and yoghurt.
- Some bacteria are essential, for example, in helping to boost our immunity.
- A healthy gut can contain 1 kilogram of bacteria.
- One housefly can carry two million bacteria.
- There are 400 times more bacteria on the average work surface than on the average toilet seat.

Helpful and harmful bacteria

Helpful bacteria

Not all bacteria are harmful. Bacteria can actually help to keep us healthy in the following ways:

- **By protecting our skin**. Some bacteria live on our skin and protect us from many harmful agents. The drier areas, like the back, have few bacteria whereas moist areas, like under the arm, have many more.
- **By helping in the production of certain foods**, for example yoghurt and cheese.
- **By reducing the risk of disease**. Scientists believe that bacteria actually help to lower the risk of certain cancers, heart disease and some digestive problems.
- **By helping the body to absorb calcium**. A healthy gut which has a plentiful supply of helpful bacteria helps the body to absorb calcium, which we need to keep our bones strong.
- **By protecting newborn babies**. Certain helpful bacteria are particularly important for newborns, whose immune defences have not yet had time to develop properly. Breast milk contains substances which help the growth of these helpful bacteria. Bottle-feeding is not as effective and breast-fed babies are more resistant to stomach upsets and diarrhoea. As we grow older, the

amount of helpful bacteria in our gut falls, which is why older people tend to be more vulnerable to gut infections and stomach bugs.

- **By assisting in the decaying process**. Bacteria are essential for treating sewage, or the breakdown of vegetable matter for compost.
- **By assisting in our digestion**.

Harmful bacteria

There are two types of harmful bacteria which affect the food we eat:

- **pathogens**
- **spoilage bacteria**.

Pathogens

Pathogens cause illness and are responsible for most cases of **food poisoning**. They may be present in food in large numbers but cannot be seen and may not cause obvious changes to the food so that it still looks, tastes and smells wholesome. They include:

- salmonella
- campylobacter jejuni
- staphylococcus aureus
- bacillus cereus
- E. coli
- clostridium perfringens
- listeria
- clostridium botulinum
- bacillary dysentery (shigella).

Spoilage bacteria

Spoilage bacteria cause food to rot and decay but they do not necessarily make people ill. Although you cannot see them, these bacteria cause changes to the food which you should be able to spot – changes in smell, taste, colour and texture are usually enough to warn you that the food is not fit to eat. (Fungi, that is yeasts and moulds, also cause food spoilage – see page 23.)

How bacteria multiply

Food poisoning bacteria grow rapidly by dividing themselves in two – a process called **binary fission:** one bacterium becomes two bacteria and then two become four, and so on. Binary fission usually takes between 10 and 20 minutes. In the right conditions one bacterium could become thousands of millions of bacteria in 12 hours. (Approximately 3 million bacteria can fit on a pinhead.)

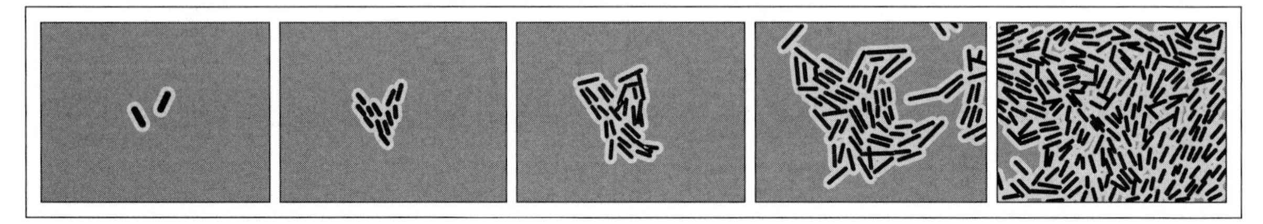

How food-poisoning bacteria multiply

The ideal conditions for food poisoning bacteria are:

- food (something for the bacteria to live on)
- warmth
- moisture
- time (sufficient time in which to multiply)
- right level of acidity (pH)
- oxygen.

Food

Bacteria can live on a wide range of foods – both raw and cooked – but prefer those which are moist and rich in nutrients (nourishment). High risk foods are those which are likely to contain pathogenic bacteria and include:

- raw meat
- cooked meat and cooked poultry – and products made from these
- milk, cream and cheese
- eggs and products made from raw eggs, for example mayonnaise
- fish and shellfish
- cooked rice
- food that is grown in or near the ground.

Poultry

Fish, Shellfish

Eggs

Rice

Unwashed fruit and vegetables

Food that is grown in (or near) the ground

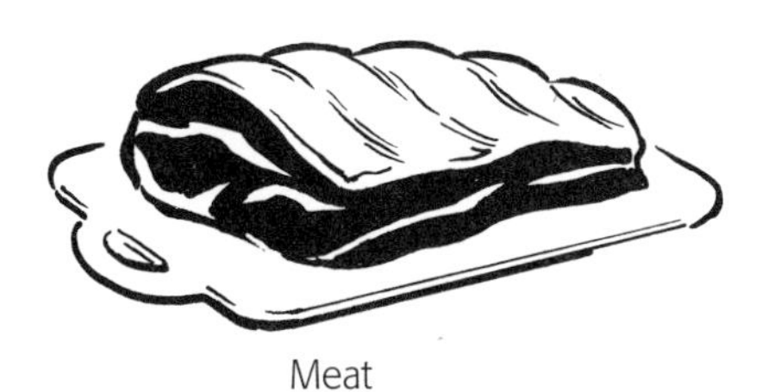

Meat

Milk, Cream, Cheese

High risk foods

Some foods, particularly raw meat and poultry, naturally contain small numbers of pathogenic bacteria. (These foods should be kept in the fridge to stop the bacteria from multiplying – see text on Warmth below.)

Warmth

Bacteria prefer warmth, particularly human body temperature (37°Celsius). For example, E. coli bacteria take 7–10 hours to double in number at a temperature of 10°C, but only 1½ hours at 20°C and just *15 minutes* at 37°C.

Putting food in the fridge stops bacteria from multiplying. If a food is already contaminated with a small number of bacteria and it is left out of the fridge overnight, it could be seriously contaminated by the next day. Then just one mouthful could make you ill.

Quick facts

- The **temperature danger zone** is 8°C – 63°C. This is the temperature range in which pathogens will multiply. When food is held within this zone, bacteria will multiply and could cause food poisoning.
- Food poisoning bacteria are killed at temperatures of 70°C and above.
- Food poisoning bacteria stored below 8°C multiply slowly; some may even die.

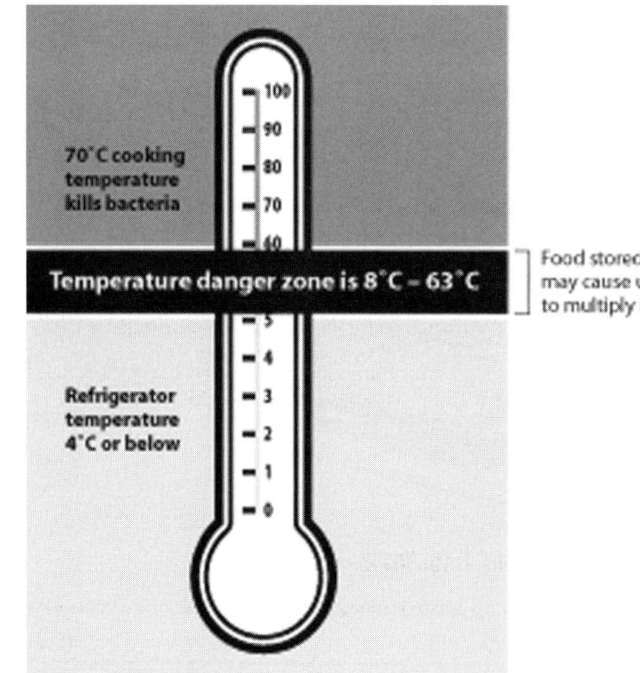

The temperature danger zone

Moisture

Most foods contain enough moisture to allow bacteria to grow. **Dehydrated** foods, such as soup mixes and powdered milk, are resistant to bacteria until water is added. A technique to remove excess water from food is to add either sugar (e.g. jam) or salt (e.g. bacon).

Time

In *ideal* conditions bacteria can double their numbers every 10–20 minutes and in eight hours *one* bacterial cell could multiply and become four million bacteria.

Right level of acidity (pH)

Most bacteria like food that is neutral in acidity (with a pH value of 7), such as milk or cheese, and will not grow in foods with a pH below 4.5, for example foods containing vinegar (such as pickles) or lemon juice. (However, if pathogens are introduced into an acid food, they may not necessarily die off immediately and could still cause illness).

Oxygen

Bacteria vary in their need for oxygen. Those which require oxygen are called aerobes and those which do not are called anaerobes. Some bacteria can grow whether they have oxygen or not.

Oxygen needs of bacteria

Aerobes (need oxygen)	**Anaerobes (do not need oxygen)**	**Grow with or without oxygen**
Bacillus cereus	Clostridium perfringens	Salmonella
	Clostridium botulinum	Staphylococcus aureus

Spores, toxins and viruses

Spores

Certain bacteria are able to form **spores**. These help the bacteria to protect themselves because spores are able to survive in conditions which would normally kill active bacteria, that is, high temperatures and a lack of moisture. When spores germinate (develop and grow) they produce pathogenic bacteria which can multiply. Examples include:

- bacillus
- clostridium.

When you cook food containing spore-forming bacteria, the bacteria will turn into spores. Spores are harmless when eaten, however if food is cooled too slowly the spores will turn back into bacteria. The bacteria will then be able to grow and multiply again. Spores can resist high temperatures, even boiling, for many minutes. They then lie inside the food waiting for the right conditions to start growing.

Toxins

Some bacteria can produce poisons known as **toxins** which stay in the food and can cause food poisoning. Examples include:

- staphylococcus aureus
- clostridium botulinum
- bacillus cereus.

(For information on these food poisoning bacteria, see Chapter 3, pages 36–7 and page 41.)

Viruses

Viruses are even smaller than bacteria and can only be seen through an electron microscope. They are difficult to spot in the laboratory as most viruses which cause food poisoning only multiply in *human* cells.

Viral food poisoning can be caused by contamination of food by infected food handlers, either from faeces or vomit. If the food is cooked, these viruses are destroyed, but contaminated ready-to-eat foods or undercooked foods can cause illness.

Foods most commonly associated with viral food poisoning are shellfish, such as cockles, mussels, oysters and clams. This is because shellfish are 'filter' feeders – that is, they filter their food through the water. If they feed in water contaminated by sewage, the viruses sit inside their bodies. Shellfish are often eaten raw or lightly cooked which does not kill the viruses and may lead to food poisoning.

Moulds and yeasts

Moulds are fungi which commonly occur on damaged fruit, vegetables, stale breads and cakes. They play an essential role in the decomposition (break down) of most organic matter.

Moulds:

- require plenty of moisture and oxygen to grow
- can produce toxins in food and can cause food poisoning – you have probably seen greenish mould growing on bread or cheese
- are destroyed by heat.

Yeasts are fungi which are used in a controlled way to ferment beer, wine, cider and soy sauce. They are also used in bread making, as flavouring agents and in Marmite®.

Yeasts:

- prefer acidic conditions and plenty of oxygen
- are found in soil and on the surface of fruits
- can cause **spoilage** of food by souring wine or fruit juices, for example when wild yeasts from the air get into opened containers
- do not normally cause food poisoning
- are easily destroyed by heat.

Spoilage organisms

Food spoilage is the effect of certain moulds, yeasts or bacteria which cause food to decay or 'go off'. These micro-organisms are not necessarily the bacteria which can cause food poisoning.

Usually your senses – sight, smell and taste – will warn you that food is spoilt or 'off'. The main signs to look out for include the following:

- Odour. 'Off' odours are smells which are produced when bacteria break down food, for example the smell of rotten eggs
- Sliminess. As bacteria multiply, the food can become slimy. Moulds may also form slimy 'whiskers'.

- Discoloration. Some moulds have coloured spores which give the food a distinctive colour, for example black pin mould on bread, or blue and green mould on citrus fruit and cheese.
- Souring. Foods go sour when certain bacteria produce acids, for example when milk separates and sours from the production of lactic acid.
- Gas. Bacteria and yeasts often produce gas which can affect food, for example yoghurt pots 'blow' or have domed lids, meat becomes spongy, packages and cans swell or have a popping or fizzing sound on opening.

How foods spoil

Eating food during the early stages of the spoilage process should not make you ill, although it probably will not taste or smell very good. Food safety experts recommend that you never scrape the mould off food – throw it away! Mould is not just on the surface, it 'penetrates' the food.

Knowledge Test

Match the terms with the definitions below.

Term	Definition
1 Viruses	**a** The process by which a single bacterium multiplies by splitting in two.
2 Spore	**b** Fungi which occur on the surface of foods such as fruit and stale bread.
3 Pathogen	**c** Foods which are particularly likely to encourage the growth of food poisoning bacteria.
4 Spoilage	**d** Micro-organisms which are smaller than bacteria.
5 Temperature danger zone	**e** A protective coating formed by some bacteria which enables them to live in poor conditions.
6 High risk foods	**f** The process by which food decays, making it unacceptable to eat.
7 Binary fission	**g** The range of temperatures at which most bacteria multiply – above 5°C and below 63°C.
8 Moulds	**h** An organism which causes disease.

(Answers on page 177.)

Chapter 3

The causes of food poisoning

This chapter looks at the causes of food poisoning. It describes the different categories of food poisoning organisms and how they can make you ill. Some of the names of food poisoning illnesses, such as salmonella, will be familiar to you, but there are many more. For each food poisoning organism you will look at the steps that can be taken to prevent illness.

This chapter covers the following topics:

- ❑ Categories of food poisoning.
- ❑ How bacteria from food sources can make you ill.
- ❑ How to recognise food poisoning.
- ❑ Bacterial causes of food poisoning.
- ❑ Viral causes of food poisoning.
- ❑ What is food-borne disease?

Categories of food poisoning

Food poisoning can be split up into different categories, or types:

- ➤ Natural food poisoning. This is caused by some plants and fish which are toxic (poisonous) to humans, for example rhubarb leaves, certain types of mushrooms, puffer fish.

- Chemical food poisoning. This is caused by chemicals getting into food, for example through the over-use of insecticides, via cleaning agents, and through the heavy metal contamination of fish from industrial areas.

- Bacterial food poisoning. This is caused by bacterial contamination of food and is the most common form of food poisoning.

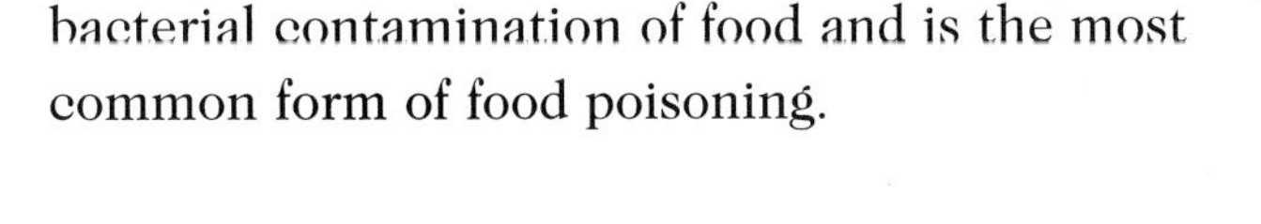

- Viral food-borne infection. Viruses are carried in food to the human body where they then multiply, for example Hepatitis A and Norwalk Virus.

- Mycotoxin poisoning. This is caused by moulds which produce toxins called mycotoxins. You may have heard of food poisoning caused by aflotoxin which grows in damp wheat and peanuts.

- Protozoan infections. These micro-organisms often occur in water.

- Worm infections. These infections can be caused by roundworms, tapeworms and flukes and can cause stomach pain and diarrhoea.

The two categories of food poisoning covered below are those caused by bacterial and virus infection.

How bacteria from food sources can make you ill

Pathogens can either already be present in food, or can come from other people, surfaces or equipment, or other food by **cross contamination**. The main causes of bacterial food poisoning and what to do to prevent it happening are shown in the table below:

Causes and prevention of bacterial food poisoning

Cause	Example	What to do
Undercooking	When the oven is not hot enough (or used for long enough) to ensure that meat or chicken is completely cooked	Frozen raw meat and poultry must be properly thawed before thorough cooking to ensure that pathogenic bacteria are destroyed. All food should be cooked to at least 75°C.
Food prepared in advance and not refrigerated	A ham sandwich left out of the fridge – uncovered or covered – for several hours	All food prepared in advance must be refrigerated to reduce bacterial growth. Fridges should operate below 5°C. Food poisoning bacteria can multiply rapidly at room temperature.
Poor personal hygiene	A person preparing food without washing their hands properly	It is important that hands are washed as frequently as necessary but definitely before handling food or equipment, after visiting the toilet, in between handling raw and cooked food and after handling waste food or refuse. Poor **personal hygiene** can result in food becoming contaminated with bacteria.
Cross contamination	A knife used to cut raw meat is not washed and is then used to cut cooked or ready-to-eat food	Food poisoning bacteria may be present in raw food such as meat and poultry. If these bacteria are allowed to contaminate food which is to be eaten without further cooking, food poisoning can result. Cross contamination from raw food may happen as a result of poor storage, when the juices from raw meat are allowed to drip on to cooked food, or via a chopping board, work surface or utensils used for both raw and cooked food. Food handlers must wash their hands and equipment after handling raw meat.
Failure to keep cooked food hot	Serving food which has been allowed to stand and become cool – below 63°C – after cooking	Hot food should be kept above 63°C. As thorough cooking does not destroy spores, hot food kept below this temperature can allow the spores to germinate and produce food poisoning bacteria.
Infected food handlers	A person who returns to work after vomiting and diarrhoea may still be a **carrier** of food-poisoning bacteria	Anyone suffering from a gastrointestinal illness (vomiting, diarrhoea, and so on) should not prepare and/or serve food for others until totally clear of symptoms for at least 48 hours. Even then, very thorough hand washing is essential. Boils and cuts which have turned septic are another source of pathogens. Wounds should be completely covered and protected by a waterproof dressing.
Eating food from unsafe sources	Buying high risk foods from a supply vehicle which does not have proper refrigeration	Only buy chilled foods stored in refrigerated cabinets.

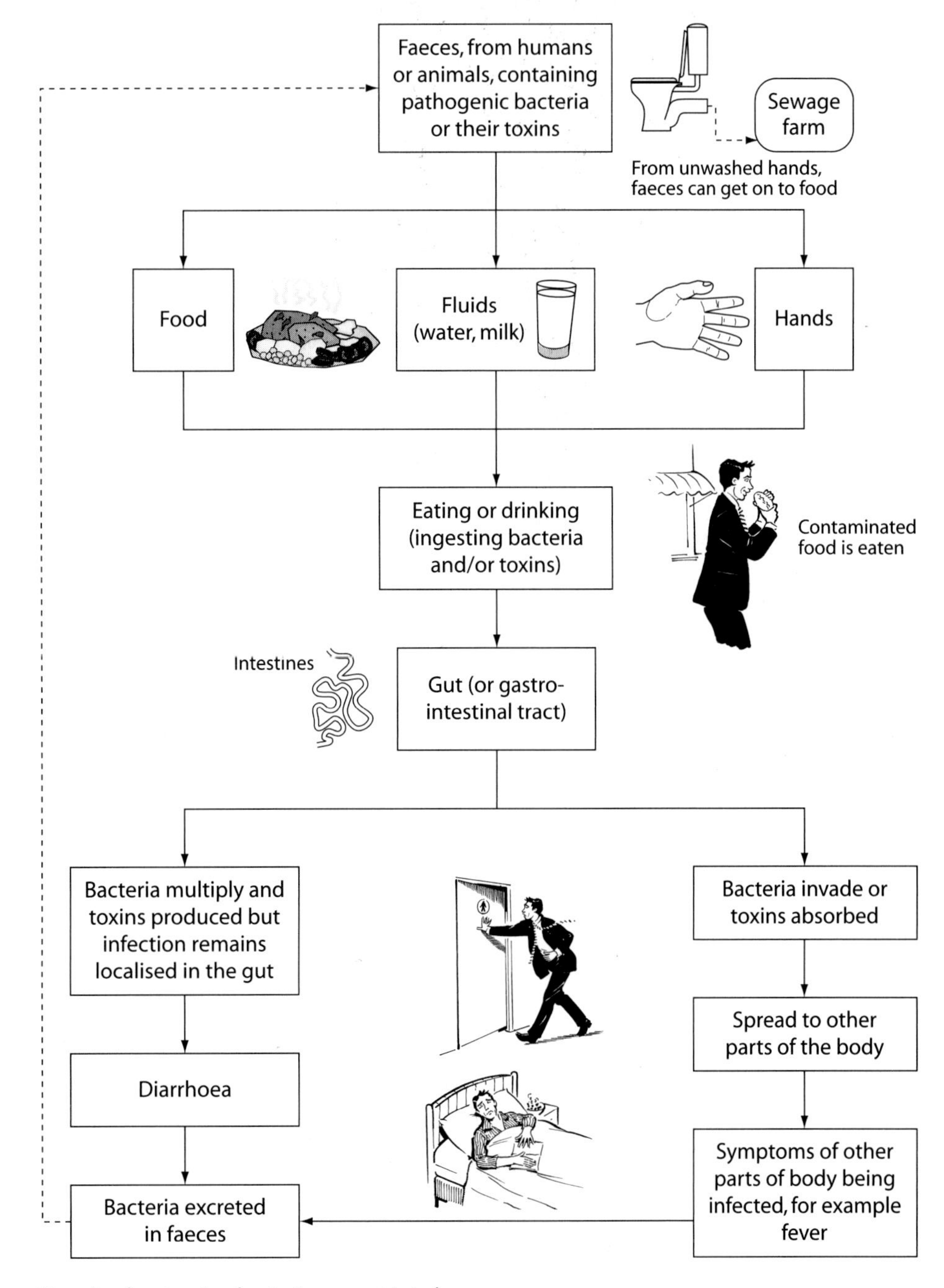

How food poisoning bacteria can get into humans

How to recognise food poisoning

It can be difficult to tell when pathogenic bacteria in food have made you ill. For instance, it is hard to tell if food is unsafe because you cannot see, smell or taste the bacteria it may contain. Sometimes you might think that it must be the meal you ate last that has caused the sickness. In fact, there is a wide range of time between eating contaminated food and the onset of illness. Usually, the bacteria or viruses take 1–3 days to cause the symptoms. However, symptoms could appear as soon as 20 minutes after eating certain foods or as long as six weeks after. It depends upon a variety of factors, including the type of bacteria in the food.

General symptoms of food poisoning

The general symptoms of food poisoning are:

- feeling sick (nausea) and vomiting
- diarrhoea
- stomach pain
- fever
- aching limbs
- headache.

Some of the symptoms listed above can also be associated with other illnesses, so you should always contact your doctor if they persist. The actual sickness can last for up to five days or even longer, depending on the type of bacteria.

Incubation period

When someone swallows bacteria that cause food poisoning there is a delay, or **incubation period**, before symptoms begin. This is because most bacteria which cause food poisoning need *time* to multiply in the intestine, or gut. The length of the incubation period depends on the type of bacteria and how many are swallowed. It could be hours or days.

Bacterial causes of food poisoning

Campylobacter jejuni

This is the most common cause of bacterial food poisoning in the UK. It is classed as a food-borne infection rather than food poisoning as the bacteria do not tend to multiply in food but, once swallowed, can multiply in the gut. Also, unlike types of food poisoning which are caused by large numbers of bacteria in the body, only a *small* number of campylobacter bacteria can cause illness.

Where it may be found

It can be found in untreated milk, water and sewage, but the most common source of infection is undercooked poultry. Red meat can also be contaminated with campylobacter. Milk can be contaminated by birds, especially magpies, pecking bottle tops on the doorstep. Pets with diarrhoea can also be a source of infection.

Effects

These include fever (high body temperature), headache and dizziness for a few hours, followed by severe stomach pain and diarrhoea which may be bloody. Vomiting is rare and the illness may be mistaken for acute appendicitis because of the severity of the pain with fever. Even after recovering, the person can continue to excrete the bacteria in their stools for some time, and so particular attention to personal hygiene is important.

Keys to Good Practice: Campylobacter jejuni

- ✔ Always cook meat and chicken till piping hot right through.
- ✔ Don't allow raw meat and chicken to contaminate ready-to-eat foods.
- ✔ Don't drink water from rivers or streams.
- ✔ Make sure that birds cannot peck milk-bottle tops.
- ✔ Wash hands after handling pets.

Incubation period

Symptoms can take 1–10 days to appear (usually 2–5 days) and generally last 2–7 days.

Salmonella

Salmonella food poisoning is the second most common cause of food poisoning in the UK. Large numbers of salmonella bacteria are usually needed to cause infection, although some outbreaks have been reported where the numbers have been small. Salmonella survives when refrigerated although it may multiply more slowly. It is killed by thorough cooking and pasteurisation or specialised heat treatment.

Salmonella food poisoning may cause serious illness and even death in vulnerable people, such as babies, elderly people and those who are already ill.

Where it may be found

Salmonella can be found in raw egg or raw chicken and meat. It can also be found in unpasteurised milk, or carried by rats, mice and domestic pets. People may also be a source of these pathogens as they can continue to excrete them for a long time after recovering from a bout of salmonella food poisoning.

Effects

These include fever, diarrhoea, vomiting and stomach pain. Symptoms last for 1–8 days, but can be longer. There may be complications such as reactive arthritis.

Incubation period

Illness usually occurs within 36 hours of eating infected food.

Why is salmonella such a problem?

There are more than 2,000 different strains of salmonella bacteria and it is one of the commonest causes of food poisoning in the world. The bacteria live in the intestines of cows, poultry, pigs, pets and many wild animals. While they do not cause these animals any harm, they are dangerous to humans.

Keys to Good Practice: Salmonella

- ✔ Always cook eggs and chicken thoroughly.
- ✔ Avoid use of raw eggs in foods, such as mayonnaise and uncooked desserts.
- ✔ Practise good personal hygiene.
- ✔ Prevent cross contamination between raw and cooked foods.
- ✔ Keep foods at correct temperatures.
- ✔ Keep animals away from foods.

What is the most common cause of salmonella food poisoning?

Chickens carry the strain of bacteria, salmonella enteritidis, which is the single most common cause of salmonella food poisoning in the UK. The carrier chickens have no obvious symptoms, but a human who has eaten undercooked, infected eggs or infected chicken meat will suffer stomach cramps, diarrhoea, nausea, and fever.

One of the reasons for the high number of salmonella infections is thought to be the result of modern farming methods. Battery conditions, where hundreds of thousands of chickens are bred close together, enable the bacteria to infect large numbers of birds. It is important to note that the number of reported cases of salmonella has reduced dramatically due to changes in production and the introduction of vaccinations. Eggs stamped with a 'lion' have come from vaccinated chickens.

How does salmonella infect humans?

The most *direct* methods by which salmonella bacteria can be spread to humans are:

- ➤ by eating the undercooked meat of an infected animal
- ➤ by ingesting (taking in) faeces containing bacteria from the carrier's intestine, or gut. For example, in the home contaminated faeces trodden into a carpet could unknowingly pass on salmonella to a young child or a pet.

There are also *indirect* ways in which we can get salmonella bacteria:

- ➤ Fruit and vegetables that have been contaminated by water containing infected sewage carry the bacteria. If any animal or human eats the fruit and vegetables, they will become infected.

- If an infected animal is eaten by another animal or human, it too will become infected. In this way salmonella bacteria spread throughout the food chain.

How our bodies fight infection from salmonella bacteria

Once the bacteria enters the human body, it immediately starts to defend itself – see the flow chart on page 35.

Treatment

Usually, it is best to leave the body to get rid of salmonella bacteria on its own:

- Drinking plenty of fluids, preferably water, will help to stop **dehydration** and the resulting headaches.
- Painkillers can be used to treat the headaches and muscle pain.
- Anti-diarrhoeal tablets should *not* be taken. This is because diarrhoea is one of the body's main defences against the infection. Although stopping the diarrhoea will make the sufferer feel more comfortable in the short-term, it also gives the salmonella a chance to continue growing and spreading.

The use of antibiotics is not normally recommended because:

- they tend to increase the length of time that the salmonella remains in the stomach and faeces
- they prolong the symptoms of the disease and increase the risk that the salmonella may be passed from one carrier to another
- they also kill the 'friendly' bacteria in the gut that aids digestion.

However, if the infection spreads from the intestine, or if the sufferer is very old, very young or has another illness, antibiotic treatment may be necessary.

Treating infected farm animals

In farm animals salmonella is becoming increasingly difficult to treat. Antibiotics are often used but the salmonella bacteria are becoming resistant to them. Also, the use of growth-promoting antibiotics in farm animals has led to an increase in salmonella food poisoning. These special antibiotics destroy the normal digestive bacteria which would normally help protect against the salmonella bacteria. Some farmers are now vaccinating their animals against salmonella which is proving to be very successful.

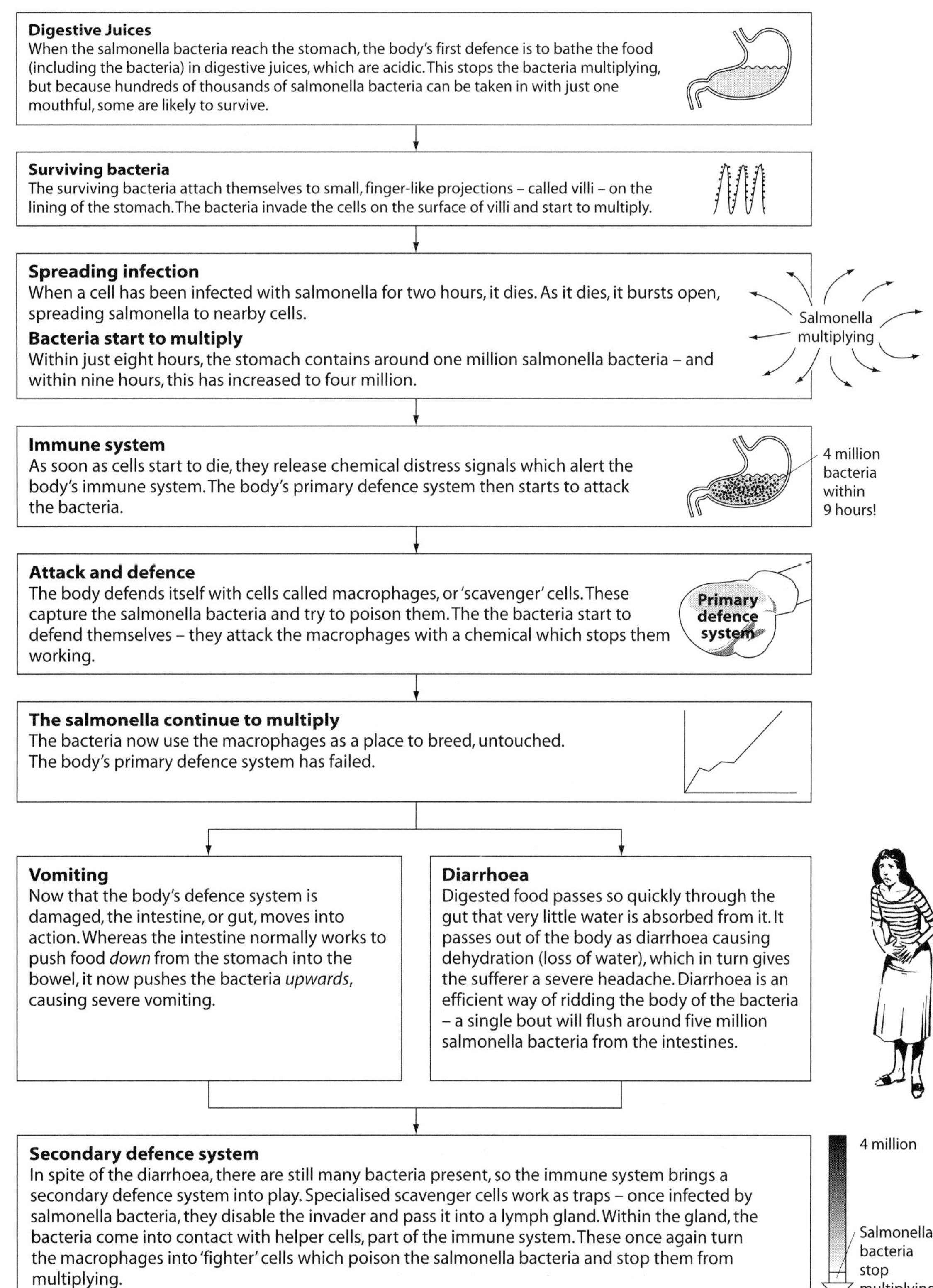

How the human body fights salmonella infection

Why is salmonella infection so dangerous?

In most cases the body is able to rid itself of salmonella bacteria within 5–7 days. However, in a small number of cases the disease takes hold and can kill. About 50 people in the UK die each year from salmonella poisoning. Those most at risk are people whose immune systems are unable to fight the effects of the bacteria quickly or effectively – the old, the very young and those who are already suffering from an illness.

Staphylococcus aureus

Food poisoning from staphylococcus aureus is the most common type of food poisoning linked with human contamination of food. Staphylococci produce heat-resistant toxins which cause illness when the food is eaten. The bacteria are destroyed by **pasteurisation** of milk and cooking of food, but the toxin may survive these processes.

Where it may be found

Staphylococcus is carried naturally on the skin of healthy people and in the nose and throat of almost half the population. It can be passed to food from your nose, hands, cuts and boils. It can easily get on to food if you sneeze without covering your nose or if you touch food after scratching your nose or face. It is also sometimes found in unpasteurised milk. It is most likely to be found on cooked meats which have been handled, milk products and gravies.

Effects

These include severe vomiting, stomach pains, lower than normal temperature and sometimes diarrhoea. Symptoms may last 6–24 hours.

Keys to Good Practice: Staphylococcus aureus

- ✔ Keep your hands away from your nose and hair while preparing food.
- ✔ Avoid coughing and sneezing near food.
- ✔ Wash your hands thoroughly before preparing and eating food.
- ✔ Always cover cuts and boils.

Incubation period

The onset of symptoms occurs between 1 and 6 hours after contamination.

Bacillus cereus

Bacillus cereus bacteria can form **spores**. These are not easily destroyed by heat and will survive cooking of food. If food is cooled slowly or kept warm for some time before serving, the spores will germinate and produce a toxin.

Where it may be found

Bacillus cereus is most often found in cooked rice and pasta dishes which have not been cooled quickly and effectively after cooking and during storage.

It can also – but less often – be found in:

- raw, dried or processed foods, such as cereals, cornflower, spices, and other dried foods
- the general environment including soil, air, dust, water and decaying matter
- animals
- foods such as turkey, beef, seafood, salads, potatoes, food mixes (for example sauces, soups, casseroles), milk powder, various bakery products and desserts, especially items with custard and cream.

Effects

These include nausea, vomiting, diarrhoea and stomach pain. Onset of symptoms can be very sudden, but is usually over fairly quickly. It is unlikely to be fatal.

Keys to Good Practice: Bacillus cereus

- ✔ Cook foods thoroughly.
- ✔ Cool food quickly after cooking and then keep in the fridge.

Escherichia coli 0157 (E. coli 0157)

This particular and rare variety of E. coli can cause severe illness. E. coli 0157 is known as the 'burger bug' because many people have been infected after eating burgers that are cooked on the outside but still raw on the inside. However, there is no simple way for the consumer to tell if the bacteria have been killed.

Where it may be found

E. coli may be found in raw and undercooked meat (particularly beef-burgers and steak pies), unpasteurised milk and dairy products, raw vegetables and unpasteurised apple juice. As small numbers of bacteria can cause illness, avoiding cross contamination from raw to ready-cooked foods is important.

Effects

The main symptom is diarrhoea, which may be bloody, and severe stomach cramps. In serious cases, E. coli can cause kidney failure. Young children, the elderly and people with chronic illness or depressed immune systems are more vulnerable and particularly at risk from such complications.

Incubation period

Symptoms normally take about two days to develop but may start within a day, or take up to five days to appear.

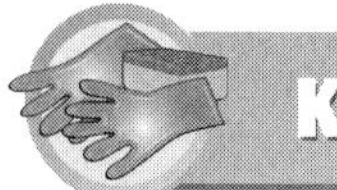

Keys to Good Practice: E. coli 0157

- ✔ Minced meat, sausages and burgers should be cooked until they are piping hot throughout, the juices run clear and no pink bits remain.
- ✔ Prevent cross contamination from raw meats to other foods.
- ✔ If caring for young children or those with poor personal hygiene, ensure their hands are washed in hot soapy water after they use the toilet or have contact with animals (including pets).

The problem with E. coli 0157

E. coli has been known for many years and most types of E. coli are quite harmless. But from time to time some strains cause illness and in the last ten years or so we have begun to recognise the particularly dangerous strain, E. coli 0157 (also called VTEC).

E. coli 0157 is still very rare. Other bacteria like salmonella and campylobacter make tens of thousands of people ill every year, whereas E. coli 0157 still only affects a few hundred. In spite of this, E.coli presents a real problem to food safety for the following reasons:

- It seems to be getting more common. No one really knows why, but the same is true all around the world.
- It needs only a small dose to make you ill.
- It is dangerous. An E.coli 0157 attack is much more likely to have serious results. Its toxin, or poison, causes very unpleasant diarrhoea, but it can also lead to more serious problems. Around 5 per cent of cases and sometimes more develop a life-threatening kidney disease known as Haemolytic Uraemic Syndrome (HUS).

How E. coli spreads

E. coli 0157 usually starts in the intestines of humans and animals, especially cattle and sheep. The most common contamination takes place in the slaughterhouse when careless dressing of the carcass splits the guts and contaminates the meat. Another factor may be dirty animals arriving at the abattoir covered in faeces due to overcrowding and stress during transport and in the holding pens.

Even if meat is contaminated, it should still be safe if it is properly cooked. Many cases of E. coli food poisoning have resulted from undercooking of foods, especially meat products such as burgers. Also it is very easy to re-contaminate meat after cooking.

In the Scottish outbreak of E. coli food poisoning in 1996:

- almost 500 people fell ill
- 127 were so ill they were admitted to hospital
- 13 needed kidney dialysis
- 21 people died.

Many of those who ate the contaminated food were very elderly. Those who died ranged from 69 to 93 years.

This serious outbreak appears to have been caused by re-contaminated meat. Scientists found E. coli on equipment used for cooked meat. This included a boiler and a vacuum-packing machine. The basic rule to keep all raw meat well away from ready-to-eat food was not followed.

Not all E.coli outbreaks have involved beef, or even meat:

- In the USA in 1996, 66 people were taken ill and one child died after drinking apple juice. The juice producer picked some apples from the ground and cattle had been grazing in the orchard.
- In the UK in 1997, dozens of guests at a wedding were infected. Lamb kebab was the cause. Some surveys show more E. coli 0157 in lamb than beef.
- Several outbreaks in the UK have involved unpasteurised milk. Poor hygiene in the dairy allows contamination during milking. It is not just the meat of cattle that can become contaminated.
- Nine people attending the 1997 Glastonbury festival got E. coli from cattle manure. Cattle were grazing in the fields until shortly before the event.
- In Japan in 1996, nearly 10,000 people became ill in a series of outbreaks after eating a type of beanshoot or radish sprout. Initial cases came from school meals.

Clostridium perfringens

Clostridium perfringens produces harmful spores, which may not be killed during cooking and reheating. Outbreaks are often linked to large-scale catering where food is prepared in advance.

Where it may be found

The bacteria may be found in gravy, cooked meat dishes, stews and pies and very large joints of meat and poultry. It is also found in animal and human faeces, dust and soil.

Effects

These include stomach pain, diarrhoea and nausea, although vomiting is rare. The illness usually lasts 12–48 hours.

Incubation period

This is usually 12–18 hours.

Keys to Good Practice: Clostridium perfringens

- ✔ Food that is not to be eaten immediately following cooking must be cooled rapidly, then refrigerated to prevent the spores developing.
- ✔ The food must be reheated quickly and thoroughly to kill any bacteria produced by the spores.
- ✔ Do not reheat food more than once.
- ✔ Keep raw foods, including vegetables – which may be contaminated with infected soil – away from other foods.

Clostridium botulinum

This spore-forming (heat-resistant) bacterium is very dangerous although it is very rare nowadays. It produces a toxin which causes a severe illness called botulism, which has a high death rate.

Where it may be found

It is found in soil, meat, fish and vegetables. It prefers an oxygen-free environment, normally found in canned and vacuum-packed meats or fish, to produce its powerful toxin.

Effects

At first, it causes a short bout of diarrhoea and vomiting, but then symptoms may disappear. The toxin can also cause difficulties in swallowing and breathing and may lead to paralysis or even death if untreated. The illness can last for 6–8 months.

Incubation period

This may be from 2 hours to 8 days, but is usually 12–36 hours.

Keys to Good Practice: Clostridium botulinum

- ✔ Do not use damaged or 'blown' cans of food.

Listeria

Unlike most other food poisoning bacteria, listeria can grow at low temperatures (below 3°C). It can survive vacuum packing and microwave cooking. The people most at risk from the dangers of listeria are pregnant women, the very young, the elderly or people with weakened immune systems. In the UK an estimated 300 people become seriously ill with listeriosis each year, and of these about 75 die.

Where it may be found

Listeria is usually found in unpasteurised milk, feta cheese and other soft-rind cheese. It is also found in delicatessen and other ready-to-eat foods, including hot dogs and meat slices, and in unwashed salad vegetables.

Effects

Listeriosis produces flu-like symptoms and is a serious risk for pregnant women as it can lead to blood poisoning, miscarriage and stillbirth and can cause the birth of an infected child.

Incubation period

The symptoms can take 3–70 days to appear.

Keys to Good Practice: Listeria

- ✔ Store foods at correct temperatures.
- ✔ People who are at risk of infection should not eat pâté or soft cheeses.
- ✔ Use foods within the recommended shelf-life.
- ✔ Cook-chill meals and ready-to-eat poultry must be heated thoroughly until piping hot.

Food poisoning bacteria and their diseases

Bacteria	Natural source	Other food or drink source	Incubation period	Typical patient	Effects of illness
Salmonella	Chickens, eggs, ducks, turkeys	Many prepared foods, especially cooked meats	12–36 hours	Anyone, but especially the very young and elderly people	Diarrhoea, vomiting, abdominal pain, fever
Campylobacter	Poultry, meat, unpasteurised milk	Water	2–5 days	Particularly young, healthy adults	Diarrhoea (often bloody), abdominal pain, nausea, fever
Staphylococcus aureus	Unpasteurised milk, human body – especially skin, nose, mouth, cuts, spots and boils	Any food can be contaminated through food handling by infected person	1–6 hours	Anyone	Abdominal pain, mainly vomiting, some diarrhoea, subnormal body temperature
Listeria	Soil, animal manure, water	Chilled and processed foods, cooked chicken, salamis, pâté, soft-crusted cheeses and salad vegetables	1–70 days	Pregnant women, the elderly, immuno-suppressed people, some young healthy adults	Flu-like symptoms with fever and diarrhoea, miscarriage of pregnancy, stillbirth and (rarely) septicaemia, meningitis
E. coli	Cattle and sheep, sewage, water, unpasteurised milk	Raw meat, burgers and sausages	12–24 hours or longer	Children and elderly people	Abdominal pain, some diarrhoea, vomiting
Bacillus cereus	Widely in the environment in soil and dust	Cereals, especially cooked rice	1–5 hours or 8–16 hours depending on the type of food poisoning	Anyone	Abdominal pain and diarrhoea, vomiting
Clostridium perfringens	Animal and human excreta, soil dust, insects	Raw meat	12–18 hours	Anyone	Abdominal pain and diarrhoea. Vomiting is rare
Clostridium botulinum	Soil, vegetables, fish	Damaged cans of fish, vegetables, processed meat and vegetables	12–36 hours	Anyone	Difficulties in breathing, swallowing, double vision, progressive paralysis. Death is common or very slow recovery

Viral causes of food poisoning

Norovirus infection

Noroviruses or small round structured viruses (SRSV) are a group of viruses. The first one to be found was in the USA where the Norwalk virus caused an outbreak of acute viral **gastro-enteritis** in the county of Norfolk. SRVS are the most common food-borne *viral* infection and are spread mainly from one infected person to another. SRSV illness occurs more frequently in adults and older children than in the very young.

Source of outbreaks

Water is the most common source of outbreaks and may include water from public supplies, wells, swimming pools, and water stored aboard cruise ships. The foods most often causing SRSV outbreaks are shellfish and salad ingredients. Infected kitchen workers can contaminate a salad or sandwich as they prepare it if they have the virus on their hands.

Effects

Only a small amount of the virus can cause illness, which is usually mild and includes nausea, vomiting, diarrhoea and stomach pain. The sufferer may also have a headache and a low-grade fever. The illness normally only lasts about 2 days.

Incubation period

The illness develops 24–48 hours after contaminated food or water is eaten.

The good news about this virus is that it doesn't multiply in foods like many other bacteria do. Also, it is destroyed by thorough cooking.

Keys to Good Practice: Noroviruses

- ✔ Cook food thoroughly.
- ✔ If you are travelling in an area that appears to have polluted water, drink pasteurised milk or bottled drinks without ice.
- ✔ Good personal hygiene will limit the spread of infection.

What is food-borne disease?

Food-borne disease is an illness which can be spread by food or water. Unlike food poisoning, a food-borne disease only needs very small numbers of micro-organisms to cause the illness, and the organisms do not need food in which to multiply. The chain of infection is the same as that for food poisoning, that is, the faecal-oral route where faeces enters the body through the mouth.

Incubation period

This can be days, weeks or even months (in the case of listeria, for example). If the illness is severe, it can last for a long time – even years – because the infection enters the bloodstream, causing serious long-term health problems. Examples of food-borne diseases are:

- typhoid
- paratyphoid
- tuberculosis
- dysentery
- hepatitis A
- brucellosis.

The following three food-borne diseases are caused by bacteria:

- campylobacter
- listeriosis
- E. coli 0157.

Treatment for food-borne infections

Most food-borne infections get better without medical help. Depending on the type of bacterial infection antibiotics may be prescribed in some cases. Before doing this, the doctor will usually ask for a stool specimen for analysis so as to find out which bacterium is responsible and which antibiotic to prescribe.

Dehydration (loss of the body's water) caused by diarrhoea and vomiting should be treated immediately with oral rehydration solutions available over the counter at chemists. If these are not available you can make your own using a generous pinch of salt (1.5 g) and a teaspoon of sugar stirred into a glass of fruit juice or water (250 ml).

It is very important that infants and young children do not dehydrate. If the illness lasts more than a few days or there is blood in the stools, seek medical advice.

Knowledge Test

Choose the right answer in each case.

1 You cannot get food poisoning if you cook food thoroughly and eat it promptly.

a True **b** False

2 The first symptoms of food poisoning can occur:

a immediately
b within 2–48 hours after eating
c from 2 days to a week after eating
d any of the above.

3 Which of these groups has a greater risk of getting food poisoning than the others?

a Smokers.
b Regular antacid users.
c People who drink alcohol at least once a week.
d They all have an equally high risk.

4 How many salmonella bacteria does it take to give you food poisoning?

a As few as half a dozen.
b At least one thousand.
c At least one million.

5 Which food has been linked to outbreaks of food poisoning caused by E. coli?

a Apple juice **b** Minced beef
c Lettuce **d** All of the above

6 Eighty percent of all food poisoning from meat and poultry is caused by:

a E. coli
b salmonella and campylobacter
c staphylococcus
d clostridium.

7 What types of food are commonly associated with bacillus cereus food poisoning?

a Cooked rice, soups, sauces
b Chicken, fish, vegetables
c Pork, raw shell eggs, chicken
d Eggs, shellfish, lettuce

(Answers on pages 177–8.)

Chapter 4

Contamination and cross contamination

Have you every wondered why there are different coloured chopping boards in chef's kitchens? This is because the boards are used for different things, for example raw meat might be chopped on a red board while cooked meat is prepared on a blue board. The reason for this is to prevent cross contamination – the transfer of dangerous bacteria (pathogens) from one place to another.

In this chapter you will look at how cross contamination can happen and why it is important to prevent it. The chapter also looks at foods which carry a high risk of food poisoning and what can be done to keep these foods safe. Topics covered include:

- **The difference between contamination and cross contamination.**
- **What is cross contamination?**
- **Foods which carry a high risk of food poisoning.**

The difference between contamination and cross contamination

Contamination is the presence of something harmful or objectionable in food or drink which creates a risk of illness, injury or discomfort.

Cross contamination is the transfer of harmful bacteria from one food to another. Harmful bacteria can be transferred either from food to food or from hands to food.

What is cross contamination?

Cross contamination is one of the causes of food poisoning. It takes place when pathogens are transferred between food, surfaces or equipment. It can happen when bacteria from the surface of raw meat, poultry and raw vegetables with visible dirt (such as unwashed potatoes) get transferred on to **ready-to-eat food**, such as green salads, rice or pasta salads, bread or fruit. The bacteria on the raw food are killed when the food is cooked, but the ready-to-eat food gets eaten without further cooking, complete with pathogenic bacteria.

Sources of pathogens include:

- raw foods
- **food pests** – flies, rodents, birds
- people
- dust, dirt and air
- food waste
- pets.

How are bacteria transferred?

Bacteria can be transferred to food through:

- our hands
- chopping boards, knives and other cooking tools and equipment
- food contact surfaces, dish cloths and towels.

Cross contamination is most likely to happen when:

- raw food touches a high-risk food – this is *direct* contamination
- liquid or juices from a raw food drip on to a high risk food – this is *indirect* contamination
- bacteria are carried by hands or utensils from a raw food to a high risk food – this is indirect contamination.

For example:

- If the juices from raw meat drip on to a cake in the fridge, bacteria will spread from the meat to the cake.
- If you cut raw meat on a chopping board, bacteria will spread from the meat to the board and knife. If you then use the same board and knife (without washing them thoroughly) to chop a lettuce, the bacteria will spread from the board and knife to the lettuce. The meat is then cooked and the pathogens killed, but because the lettuce is not cooked it can cause food poisoning.
- If you touch raw food and then do not wash your hands thoroughly, you can spread bacteria to other things you touch.

Examples of cross contamination – transferring bacteria from a contaminated source to uncontaminated food

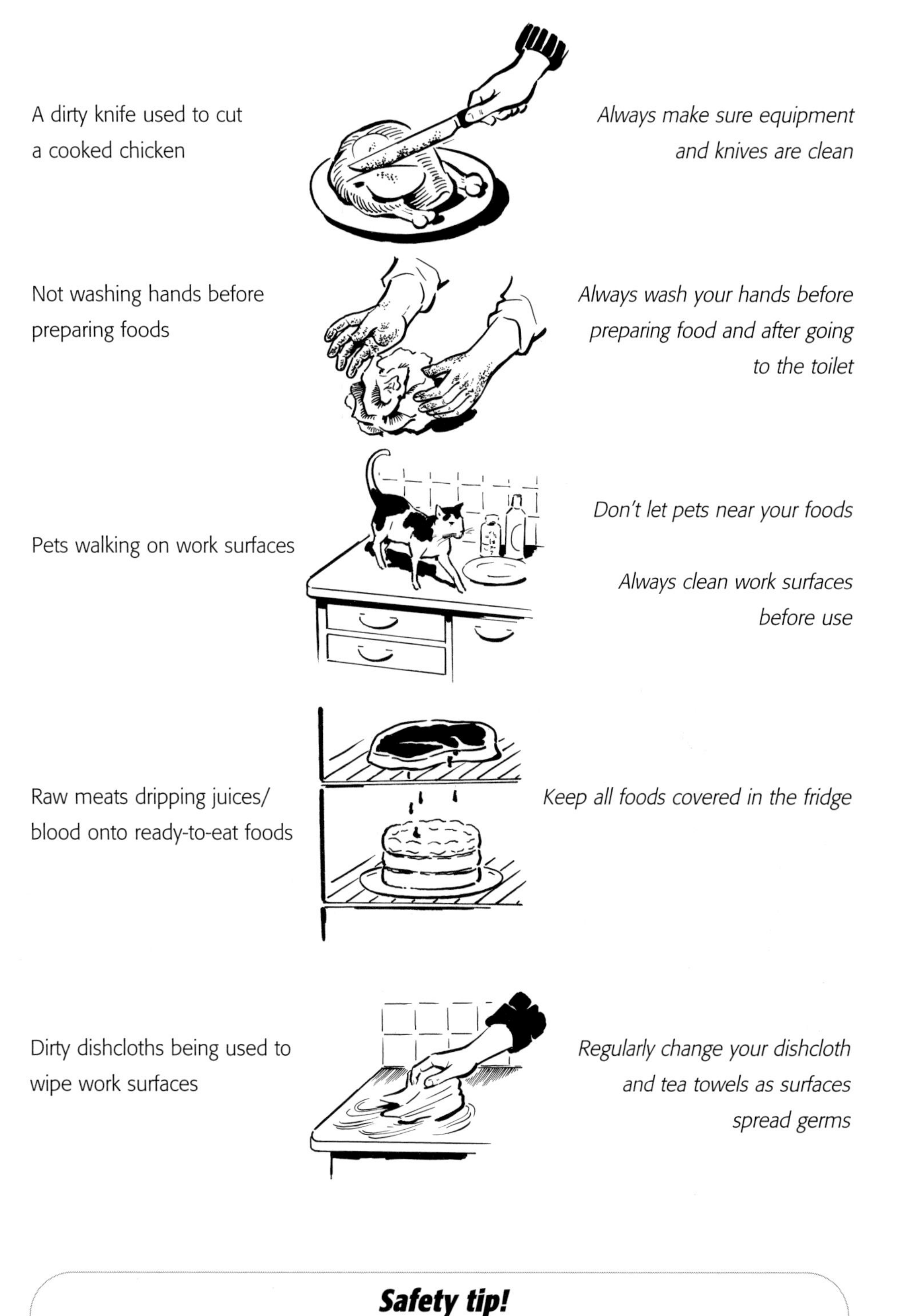

A dirty knife used to cut a cooked chicken

Always make sure equipment and knives are clean

Not washing hands before preparing foods

Always wash your hands before preparing food and after going to the toilet

Pets walking on work surfaces

Don't let pets near your foods

Always clean work surfaces before use

Raw meats dripping juices/ blood onto ready-to-eat foods

Keep all foods covered in the fridge

Dirty dishcloths being used to wipe work surfaces

Regularly change your dishcloth and tea towels as surfaces spread germs

Safety tip!

By preventing cross contamination, you can stop the spread of pathogenic bacteria.

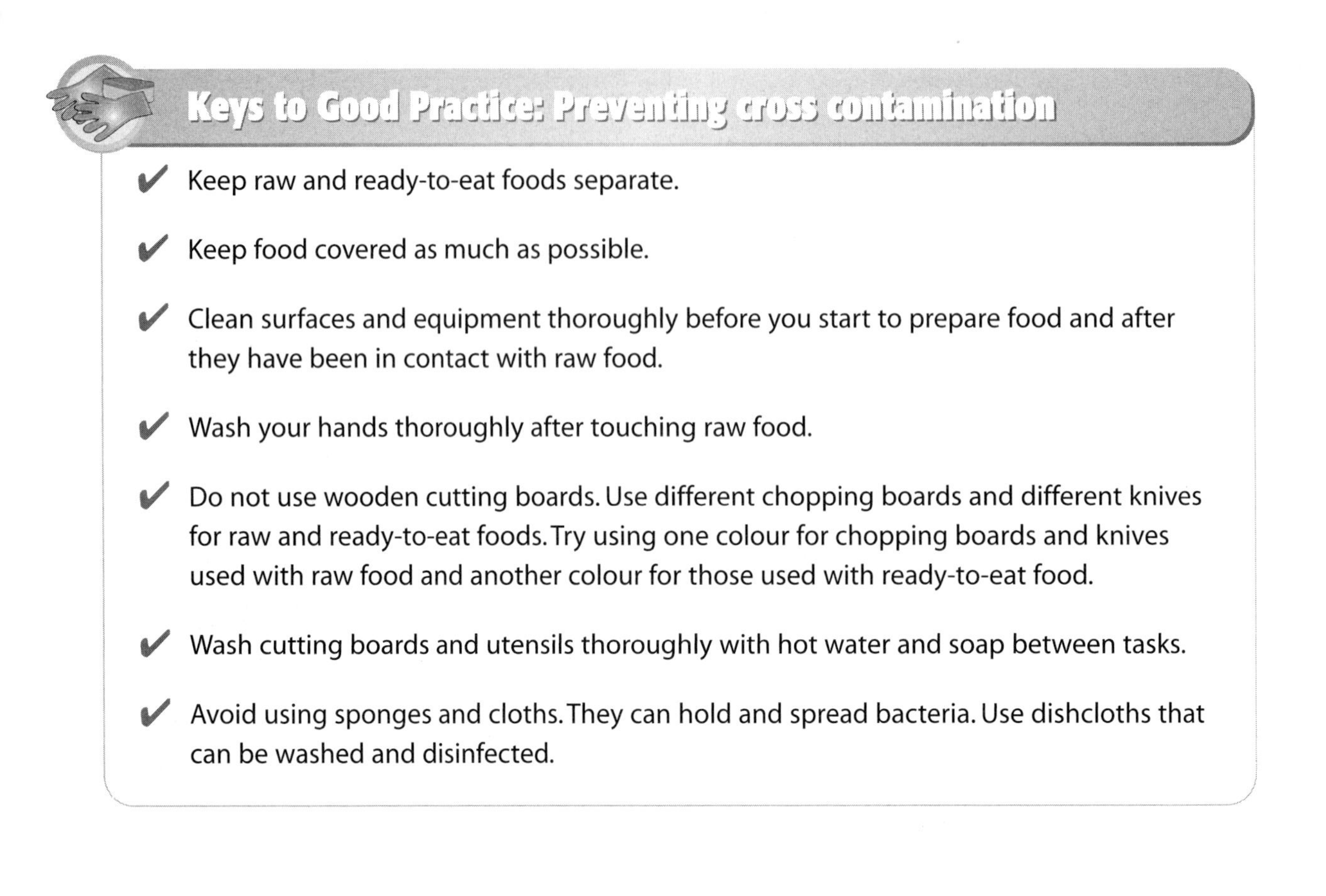

Keys to Good Practice: Preventing cross contamination

- ✔ Keep raw and ready-to-eat foods separate.
- ✔ Keep food covered as much as possible.
- ✔ Clean surfaces and equipment thoroughly before you start to prepare food and after they have been in contact with raw food.
- ✔ Wash your hands thoroughly after touching raw food.
- ✔ Do not use wooden cutting boards. Use different chopping boards and different knives for raw and ready-to-eat foods. Try using one colour for chopping boards and knives used with raw food and another colour for those used with ready-to-eat food.
- ✔ Wash cutting boards and utensils thoroughly with hot water and soap between tasks.
- ✔ Avoid using sponges and cloths. They can hold and spread bacteria. Use dishcloths that can be washed and disinfected.

Keep food covered

Keep raw and ready-to-eat foods separate

Use different chopping boards and different knives for raw and ready-to-eat foods

Foods which carry a high risk of food poisoning

These are foods that are most likely to cause food poisoning:

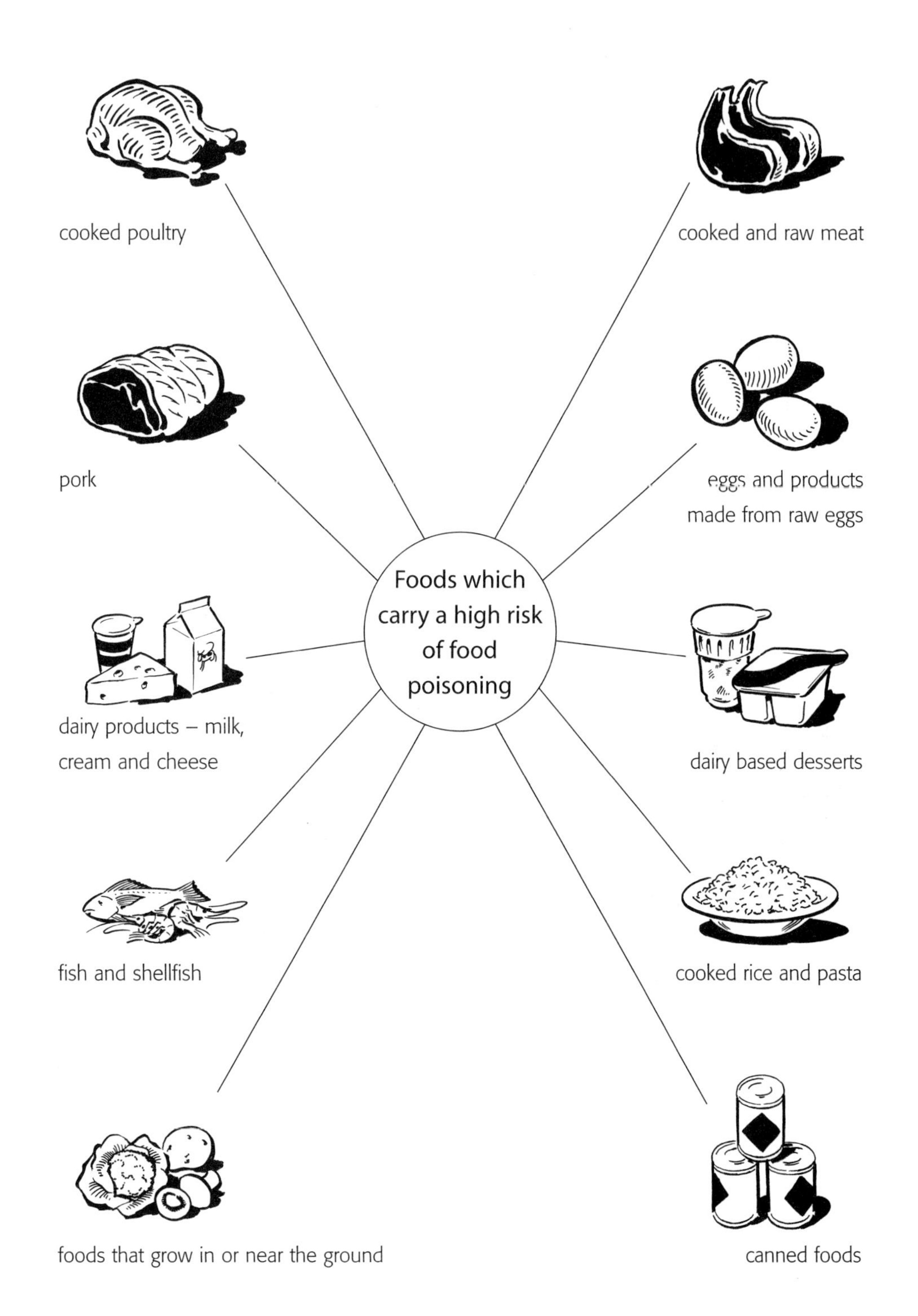

Poultry

The risks: *salmonella, campylobacter*

Chicken and turkey carry the bacteria salmonella enteritidis which is now the single most common cause of salmonella food poisoning in the UK (see Chapter 3, pages 32–6).

As well as salmonella, poultry meat can also contain campylobacter, which is now the most common bacterial cause of **gastro-enteritis** in the UK. Eating undercooked chicken, or food that has been in contact with raw chicken, can cause this disease. As with salmonella the symptoms of infection include stomach cramps, diarrhoea and fever. They can last up to a week.

How to avoid the risk of food poisoning: *See Chapter 7, page 94, for information on how to cook poultry safely to avoid the risk of food poisoning.*

Red meat

The risks: *salmonella, campylobacter, E. coli*

Red meat can contain salmonella and campylobacter. In addition, E. coli is found in the intestines of healthy cows. In the early 1980s the bacteria became known as an important cause of food-borne disease. Although it is not as common as salmonella, up to 19 per cent of people infected with E. coli 0157 develop complications, including kidney failure. More than 2 per cent of children who suffer such kidney failure die.

How to avoid the risk of food poisoning: *Scientists recommend not eating undercooked beef, which is the main source of E. coli bacteria in food. Beef should be cooked at temperatures of 75°C or higher.*

Pork

The risks: *yersinia enterocolitica, campylobacter, salmonella, E. coli*

Pork may contain the same strains of bacteria that are found in red meat. Yersinia enterocolitica, a strain of bacteria which can cause gastro-enteritis, is also found in pork. The illness is more severe in children than adults. Recovery is normally complete within 1–2 days but sometimes symptoms are mistaken for those of appendicitis, which results in a number of unnecessary operations to remove healthy appendix organs.

How to avoid the risk of food poisoning: *Yersinia enterocolitica can survive in the fridge, but it is destroyed at cooking temperatures of 75°C or above.*

Eggs

The risks: *salmonella*

As with poultry meat, eggs can be infected with salmonella.

How to avoid the risk of food poisoning:

- *Do not use cracked or dirty eggs. Check them before you buy. Eggs stamped with the Red Lion symbol have come from chickens which have been vaccinated against salmonella.*
- *Keep eggs in the fridge – only take them out about half an hour before you need to use them.*
- *Use eggs within the* ***best-before date.***
- *Wash your hands, utensils and kitchen surfaces before and after contact with eggs or foods containing eggs.*
- *Avoid eating raw eggs or runny egg yolks. Commercially prepared foods with raw eggs are safer than home-prepared ones because the commercial products contain* ***pasteurised*** *eggs, which have been heated to kill any salmonella bacteria present. Pasteurised egg in either liquid or dried form can be bought for home use if preferred.*

The Food Standards Agency recommends that the following groups of vulnerable people should eat only eggs which have been cooked until both *the white and yolk are solid:*

- *babies*
- *elderly people*
- *pregnant women*
- *people who are sick.*

Dairy products

***The risks:** salmonella, campylobacter, E. coli, listeria*

Dairy products such as milk, yoghurt and soft cheeses can contain disease-causing bacteria. Salmonella, campylobacter and E. coli are all found in dairy products. Listeria can also be found in dairy products such as soft cheeses like feta cheese, cottage cheese, Brie and Camembert.

Refrigeration does not stop the growth of listeria which makes the bacteria difficult to control. Disease caused by listeria (listeriosis) may be so mild that it goes unnoticed, though it can cause flu-like symptoms. People with low immunity, for example newborn babies or the elderly, are more likely to be affected. In fact, although death is very rare in healthy adults, 30 per cent of sufferers of listeria food poisoning who have weakened immune systems die.

Desserts

***The risks:** Dessert-related outbreaks of food poisoning are caused by bacteria in the dish's* raw *ingredients, such as eggs, fruit and milk, and also by contamination by food handlers who can cross contaminate different foods or contaminate food themselves through poor personal hygiene.*

Fish and shellfish

The risks: *vibrio bacteria, Novoviruses (or SRSVs)*

Vibrio bacteria are commonly associated with shellfish food poisoning. This is not as a result of contaminated water, however, as these bacteria are found naturally in the sea.

Symptoms are diarrhoea, nausea, stomach cramps and vomiting, but in some people infection from vibrio bacteria can cause death within two days. People who are particularly at risk include those with a weakened immune system – people with cancer, diabetes, liver disease, stomach problems or immune disorders. Raw seafood is a risk and in Japan, where many seafoods are eaten raw, this type of food poisoning is a major problem.

Other food poisoning outbreaks linked to shellfish are thought to arise from viruses – Novoviruses rather than bacteria. These viruses cause similar symptoms to those caused by bacteria. Shellfish are often found in estuaries and inlets that are also used for sewage disposal, and in this way shellfish pick up the viruses. Even good cleaning will not kill novoviruses.

Disease caused by infected fish is less common. Fish that is not fresh can smell and taste like ammonia. Although it is not dangerous, it is better not to eat fish that has a strong smell.

How to avoid the risk of food poisoning:

- *Cooking normally kills the vibrio bacteria in shellfish.*
- *Do not eat raw or partly cooked shellfish.*
- *Cook fish until it flakes and loses its translucent appearance.*

Cooked rice

See the information on bacillus cereus in Chapter 3, page 37.

Fruit and vegetables

***The risks:** salmonella, campylobacter, listeria, SRSVs*

Fruit and vegetables may be contaminated with pathogenic bacteria through the use of manure containing animal faeces and through contaminated water. Generally, however, fruit and vegetables are not a common source of food poisoning.

How to avoid the risk of food poisoning:

- *Wash all fruit and vegetables thoroughly.*
- *Do not allow soil on vegetables such as potatoes to come into contact with ready-to-eat foods.*

Canned foods

***The risks:** clostridium botulinum*

Botulism caused by clostridium botulinum bacteria is a rare but life-threatening disease. It causes death in 30 per cent of cases. The bacteria are widely found in our environment but become dangerous in certain conditions when they produce a lethal toxin. The toxin causes paralysis, and victims commonly suffocate as a result of paralysis of the lungs.

Clostridium botulinum prefers an oxygen-free environment and low acidity. Improperly canned low-acid foods, such as green beans, mushrooms, spinach, olives, beef and fish, can provide this environment.

How to avoid the risk of food poisoning:

- *Bulging cans, or canned food with a poor smell, should be avoided, though there may be no obvious signs of infection.*
- *The toxin can be destroyed by boiling food for 10 minutes.*

Case study: Food poisoning at home

Mrs Church is a Registered Childminder who cares for four children (aged between 18 months and 7 years) in her own home, between 8 am and 6 pm. She also has two older children of her own.

Mrs Church remembered to put the chicken in the fridge to defrost before she went to bed. She took it out the next morning and cut it up on the wooden cutting board her daughter had made in her design and technology class. Then she put the chicken back in the fridge to marinate until supper. She wiped the board with a cloth before she went to welcome her first day care child.

Later that morning, she chopped raw carrots and cucumber for the children's snacks on the cutting board.

The next day three of the younger children were vomiting and feeling unwell.

Questions

1. What was the likely cause of the children's food poisoning?
2. How could it have been prevented?
3. In groups, design and make a colourful poster to explain how to prevent cross contamination.

Knowledge Test

Choose the correct answer in each case.

1 How can you tell if an egg is contaminated with salmonella?

- **a** The shell is cracked.
- **b** The shell has dried chicken faeces on it.
- **c** The egg hasn't been kept refrigerated.
- **d** You can see a dark spot if you hold the egg up against a light.
- **e** Any of the above.
- **f** You can't tell.

2 You should contact a doctor for possible food poisoning if you experience:

- **a** bloody diarrhoea or pus in the stool
- **b** headache, stiff neck *and* fever
- **c** diarrhoea that has lasted for three days
- **d** weakness, numbness or tingling, usually in the arms or legs but sometimes around the mouth
- **e** any of the above.

3 Infected foods look, taste and/or smell bad.

- **a** True
- **b** False

(Answers on page 178.)

Chapter 5

Maintaining good personal hygiene

In your role as a care worker it is likely that you will be physically close to your clients at some stage. Whether you are helping them with a game or activity, helping them with their own personal needs such as walking, putting on clothes or serving their food, you will come very close to them. So it is very important that you look nice and smell nice! Being clean and neatly dressed is not only good for your clients, it will also make you feel better and more confident. Most important of all, if you work hygienically you will prevent the spread of infection and keep the workplace safer for everyone.

This chapter covers the following topics:

- ❑ **Maintaining a clean and professional appearance.**
- ❑ **Essential hand hygiene – how and when.**
- ❑ **Care in handling and breathing on food.**
- ❑ **Clean clothes and protective clothing.**
- ❑ **Jewellery and hair.**
- ❑ **Cuts and spots.**
- ❑ **Recognising and reporting personal illness.**
- ❑ **Caring for babies and young children.**
- ❑ **Following workplace rules.**

Maintaining a clean and professional appearance

When working in a care environment you need to be aware of the effect that your appearance has on clients. It is important to take care of your **personal hygiene** by showering or bathing daily. Clean clothes and shoes are also essential to a clean and tidy appearance. Some workplaces provide uniforms or protective aprons, but in less formal care situations you will be expected to dress in a tidy and professional way.

The way you dress may also be affected by the clients you are caring for. For example, dangly earrings and nose or eyebrow studs would not be suitable when working with small children or with adults who may require lifting. Long hair should be tied back to reduce the risk of infection when handling food.

Care workers should dress in a tidy and professional way

Essential hand hygiene – how and when

Even healthy people carry pathogenic bacteria on their bodies. These can be spread to the hands through touching parts of the body which contain them, such as the nose, mouth or bottom, and then from the hands to food.

Hands are the most obvious way in which food can be contaminated because they touch utensils, work surfaces and the food itself when being prepared, served or eaten. Nails can also hide dirt and bacteria. One way to prevent contamination is to keep nails short and clean and to avoid wearing nail varnish at work.

Safety tip!

Hand washing helps to stop the spread of infection.

Dirty hands can spread food poisoning bacteria all around the kitchen. Washing your hands thoroughly is a good way to reduce the chance of passing on bacteria. This should include washing the backs of hands, wrists, between the fingers and under fingernails with soap and warm water. Research has shown that many of us do not really wash our hands properly and this means that bacteria can spread to food without us being aware of it.

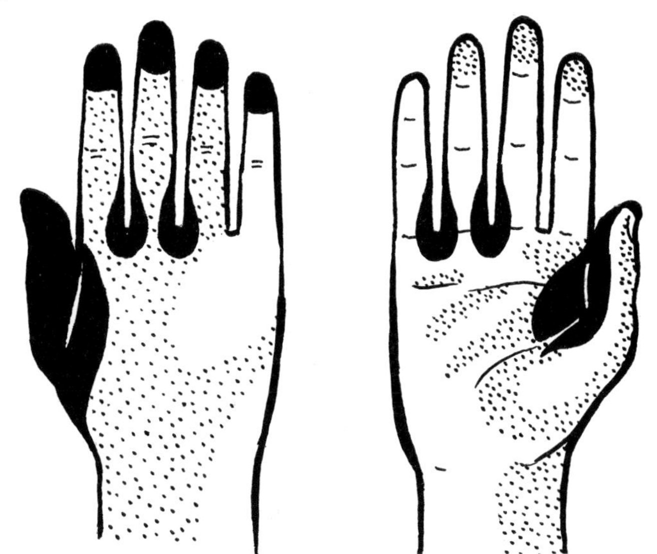

Parts of the hands frequently missed during hand washing

Quick facts

- The number of bacteria on fingertips doubles after using the toilet.
- Bacteria can stay alive on our hands for up to three hours.
- One thousand times as many bacteria spread from damp hands as from dry hands.
- Even after thorough washing, bugs such as E. coli can remain under long fingernails.
- Right-handed people tend to wash their left hand more thoroughly than their right hand, and vice versa.
- Millions of bacteria can hide under rings, watches and bracelets.
- A 1mm hair follicle can harbour 50,000 bacteria.

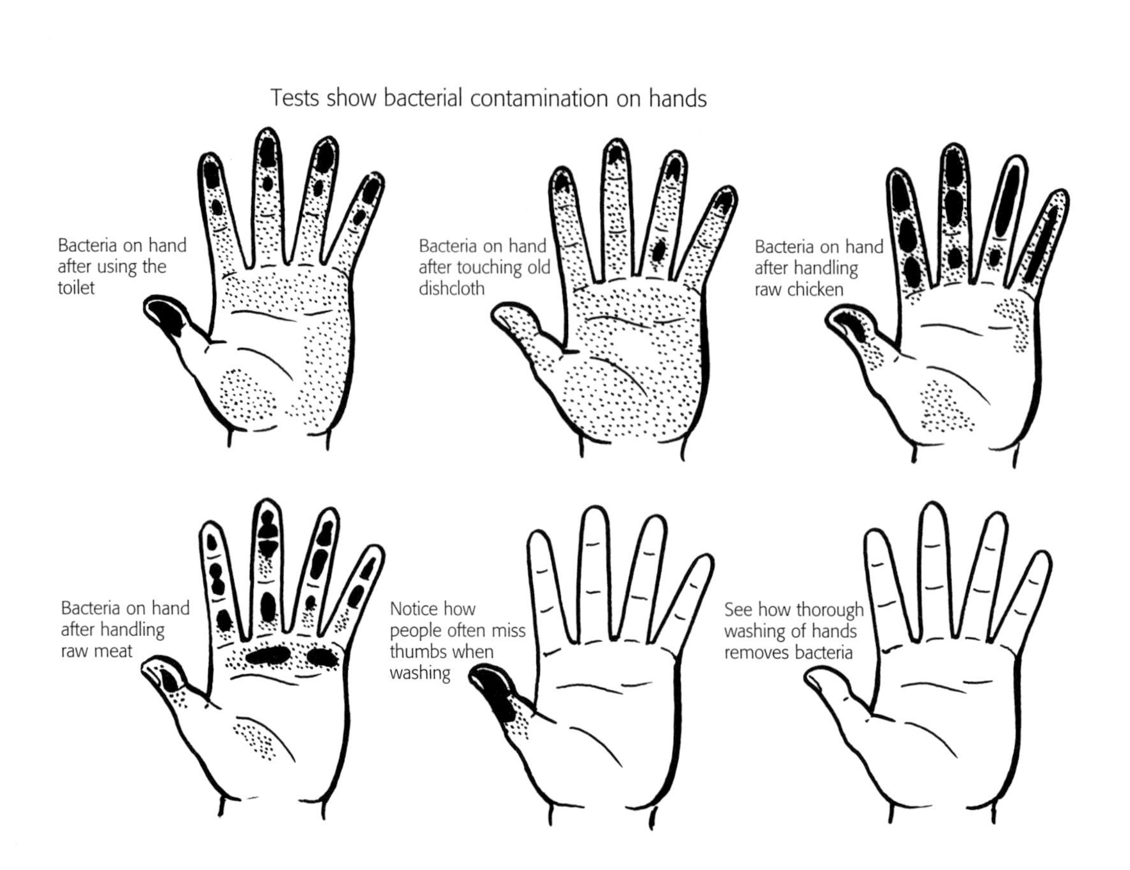

A step-by-step guide to effective hand washing

Step 1: Wet your hands thoroughly under *warm* running water and squirt liquid soap on to the palm of one hand.

Step 2: Rub your hands together to make a lather.

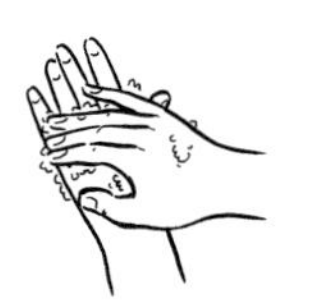

Step 3: Rub the palm of one hand along the back of the other and along the fingers. Then do the same with the other hand.

Step 4: Rub in between each of your fingers on both hands and around your thumbs.

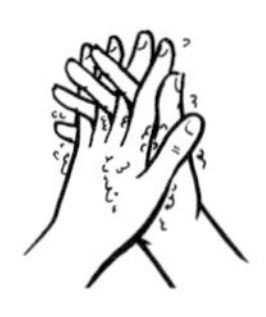

Step 5: Rinse off the soap with clean running water.

Step 6: Dry hands thoroughly on a clean dry towel, paper towel or air dryer. This should take about 15–20 seconds.

You should wash your hands regularly throughout the day, but especially at the times shown below.

Keys to Good Practice: When to wash your hands

Before:

- ✔ starting work – this is particularly important when working in a caring environment
- ✔ preparing food
- ✔ eating
- ✔ caring for the sick, changing dressings, giving medicines and so on
- ✔ looking after babies or the elderly.

Between:

- ✔ handling raw foods (meat, fish, poultry and eggs) and touching any other food or kitchen utensils.

After:

- ✔ handling raw foods, particularly meat, fish, poultry and raw eggs in their shells
- ✔ going to the toilet
- ✔ coughing or sneezing (into your hands or a tissue)
- ✔ touching your hair or face
- ✔ touching rubbish/waste bins
- ✔ changing nappies
- ✔ caring for the sick, especially those with gastro-intestinal disorders
- ✔ handling and stroking pets or farm animals
- ✔ gardening – even if you wear gloves
- ✔ **cleaning** cat litter boxes or using chemical cleansers
- ✔ smoking.

Care in handling and breathing on food

Having washed your hands, here are some more ways you can cut down the risk of contaminating food:

Keys to Good Practice: Care in handling and breathing on food

✔ Never cough or sneeze over food.

✔ Don't test food with your fingers or with a spoon which has not been washed thoroughly between each tasting.

✔ Don't blow or breathe on glasses or cutlery to help polish them.

✔ Don't smoke in food preparation areas. This is partly to prevent cigarette ends and ash from contaminating food and also because:

- people touch their lips while smoking and may transfer harmful bacteria to food
- smoking encourages coughing and droplet infection
- cigarette ends contaminated with saliva may be put on working surfaces
- every time you take food or a cigarette to your mouth you contaminate your hands with bacteria.

Clean clothes and protective clothing

Clothes can easily pick up dirt and bacteria, for example when handling pets, gardening or playing sport. Even if your workplace does not provide you with protective clothing, make sure that you follow these rules:

➤ Never wear outdoor clothes in a kitchen or food preparation area – there is a risk that they could contaminate work surfaces or food. Outdoor clothes should be stored in a locker or separate area.

➤ Always wear a clean apron or similar protective clothing if working in a food preparation area.

➤ Always wear clothes which are clean, can be easily laundered and which are appropriate to the task.

- Never wear protective clothing outside the food preparation area, for example on the way to work.

Food handlers working in food premises must:

- wear clean and washable over-clothing, preferably light-coloured and without external pockets (press-stud or Velcro fastenings are more hygienic than buttons)
- make sure that personal clothes are completely covered by protective clothing
- remove protective clothing when visiting the toilet
- never sit on a surface where food is prepared.

Note: The main purpose of protective clothing is to protect food from contamination, not to keep your clothes clean.

Jewellery and hair

If your work involves being in the kitchen all day and handling food, you would be expected to remove watches, rings and dangly earrings. Plain wedding rings and sleeper earrings are generally acceptable. You may also be required to wear a head covering or even a hairnet. The main points to remember are as follows:

- Bacteria can live on and under straps and rings. Wearing rings may prevent the thorough washing of hands.
- Small parts of jewellery such as gemstones could drop off and fall into the food.
- The hair and scalp carry bacteria, including staphylococcus aureus (see Chapter 3, page 36). Loose hairs and dandruff can fall into food and, as well as being unpleasant for the consumer, could cause contamination.
- If your hair is long it should be tied or clipped back. Never brush or comb your hair when in the kitchen or near food.
- Strong smelling perfume should not be worn as it may taint foods, especially those with a high fat content.

Cuts and spots

We all carry bacteria on our skin but these are usually present in greater numbers when we have a cut, spot or boil. The main pathogen is staphylococcus aureus which is easily spread to food (see Chapter 3, page 36). Here are some ways to help you avoid spreading bacteria:

- Cover any spot, boil or even a scratch with a waterproof plaster. Dressings should be replaced as soon as they become loose.
- Report any weeping spot or infected cut to your employer before you start work.
- In food businesses, waterproof plasters are brightly coloured – usually blue or green – so that they can be seen easily if they come off. Some plasters contain a metal strip so that they can be removed by a metal detection system if they fall off.

Recognising and reporting personal illness

If you have, or have recently had, any illness which may cause food contamination, you must report it to your manager or employer. You should also report symptoms of food poisoning to your family or close personal contacts. The following symptoms should always be reported:

- diarrhoea
- vomiting
- nausea
- ear, eye or nose discharge
- septic cuts and boils
- any skin infection.

There are good reasons for reporting these symptoms:

- If you have suffered from food poisoning you will have high numbers of pathogens in your gut which will be passed out of your body in your faeces. These bacteria can be easily transferred to toilet seats, flush handles and, of course, to your hands.

You could be a **carrier** of pathogenic bacteria and could contaminate food or other people without having any symptoms yourself. For example, if you have had salmonella food poisoning you may still have the bacteria for a long time after the symptoms have disappeared and you are feeling well.

Case study: Taking your illness to work

Kate works at Denmead residential care home where she is a care assistant. One day she comes in for her morning shift with a terrible cold. She has a runny nose and keeps sneezing. Her supervisor notices that Kate is unwell and is using tissues to wipe her nose and then throwing them away in the clients' waste bins. When it is time to serve the midday meal, the supervisor insists that Kate goes home and returns only when she is better.

Questions

1. What are the risks to the clients in Denmead if Kate stays at work?
2. Why is Kate's supervisor concerned that Kate does not help with the serving of meals?
3. What particular risks do food handlers pose when they have an infection?

Caring for babies and young children

Babies are particularly vulnerable to food poisoning. Take extra precautions if you are working with babies and young children:

- Keep the kitchen very clean – especially the floor where babies love to crawl.
- Ensure nappy changing areas are far from the kitchen.
- Always wash your hands after handling wet or dirty nappies.
- Always wipe high chairs, bibs and eating areas before and after every meal.
- Teach young children how to wash their hands and good hygiene routines from an early age.

Following workplace rules

Anyone who handles food, or whose actions could affect its safety, must follow the Regulations described in Chapter 10. This includes people who sell food (whether to retailers or to the public) and anyone who cleans articles or equipment which come into contact with food.

This means that whenever you handle food, you must follow the Regulations too. Good personal hygiene is therefore important and the way in which you work must also be clean and hygienic.

Keys to Good Practice: When handling food

- ✔ Wear clean and, where appropriate, protective over-clothes.
- ✔ Observe good personal hygiene.
- ✔ Wash your hands before handling food.
- ✔ Never smoke in food handling areas.
- ✔ Report any illness (such as infected wounds, skin infections, diarrhoea or vomiting) to your manager or supervisor immediately.
- ✔ Protect food and ingredients against contamination which is likely to make them unfit to eat or a health **hazard**. For example, uncooked poultry should not contaminate ready-to-eat foods, either through direct contact or through work surfaces or equipment.

Activity: Food safety at work

1 Find out what rules and instructions apply to food safety in your workplace.

2 At work, what precautions should you take if:

   a you have a cut or sore on your finger

   b you have a runny nose and cough

   c you have had a bout of diarrhoea and sickness?

Knowledge Test

Choose the correct answer in each case.

1 How should you always wash your hands?

   a With cold water and soap.

   b With hot water only.

   c With hot water and soap.

2 In any business where food is handled, managers must ensure their staff report any gastro-intestinal illness or any illness which may present a hazard so that potential contamination risks can be controlled. Give *four* examples of how an infected food handler might contaminate food.

3 What is the *single* most important thing you can do to prevent food poisoning?

   a Wash your hands often, especially while cooking.

   b Choose foods carefully.

   c Thoroughly cook all foods.

   d Keep the food preparation area clean.

4 Which bacteria, from someone with an unprotected finger cut who is handling a cream cake, is likely to cause food poisoning?

   a Listeria

   b Staphylococcus aureus

   c E. coli

(Answers on pages 178–9.)

Part 2

Practical food hygiene and safety

Chapter 6

Principles of safe storage

Washing your hands before preparing food and cooking food thoroughly are just two of the things you can do to protect your clients (and yourself) from food poisoning. Another is to make sure that you store food properly.

Correct storage means keeping food at the correct temperature for the right amount of time. This also avoids spoilage and preserves the food's qualities of taste, appearance and its nutritional value.

This chapter will help you to understand how to store food safely. It covers the following topics:

- ❑ **General principles of food storage.**
- ❑ **Temperature control for safe storage of hot and cold foods.**
- ❑ **Preservation of food.**
- ❑ **Stock rotation.**
- ❑ **Labelling on food.**
- ❑ **Protecting food from airborne hazards.**

General principles of food storage

Some foods may be stored at room temperature, such as:

- flour
- beans and pulses
- canned foods
- bottled foods
- cereals
- tea, coffee and spices.

Canned and dried (dehydrated) foods generally have a fairly long shelf life but they should not be stored indefinitely.

Storage of canned foods

Most canned foods have been sterilised during processing. **Sterilisation** destroys contaminating organisms present in the food.

Unopened canned foods should be stored in a cool, dry place (10°C–15°C). Although many canned foods will keep for more than 12 months, it is advisable to store them no longer than this because of uncertainty as to the true age of the food. The exceptions are canned rhubarb, fruit juices, soft drinks and some baby foods, which have a maximum storage life of about six months.

Check all labels carefully before storing food. Do not use swollen, dented or leaking cans as this indicates some failure in the processing – you should avoid tasting the food inside.

Products such as canned ham which are marked 'Store below 4°C' must be stored in the fridge. This is because the ham has not been fully sterilised. The same applies to some imported canned meats and fish products.

Storing the contents of canned food once opened

Once a can is opened, its contents should be stored in the same way as you would if the food were fresh. This is because contamination is possible as soon as the can is opened and some of the contents removed. Transfer the food to a glass or plastic container before refrigerating, and never store food in the can.

Preserved foods do not store well in open cans. For example, highly acidic or salted foods such as fruit juices or tomato products will attack the tinplate that the can is made of once open to the air.

Throw out the contents of any cans which have an unusual smell.

Storage of dried or dehydrated foods

Dehydrated foods do not readily go bad while dry but they deteriorate slowly all the time, particularly once the packet is open to the air. Dehydration slows the growth of micro-organisms by removing water, but it does not make foods sterile and these foods may carry a high level of contaminating micro-organisms which become active again in the presence of water.

Store dried or dehydrated foods in a cool place away from obvious sources of heat such as a stove or direct sunlight. Dried foods will keep in an unopened container for about six months at ambient temperatures.

Inspect regularly for insect infestation as this can be a problem.

If possible, store opened packages or dried fruits in the fridge to maintain quality for a longer period.

Rehydrated dried foods – those to which water has been added – need to be treated as highly **perishable** and kept in the fridge. They include stocks, gravies and soups which have been made from dehydrated ingredients. Once these mixes are combined with other moist ingredients, conditions are right for the growth of bacteria.

Temperature control for safe storage of hot and cold foods

Safe and unsafe temperatures

The temperature at which a food is kept for any time is extremely important. Between 8°C and 63°C is the **temperature danger zone** – this is the temperature range in which food poisoning bacteria may grow. The shorter the time that foods, including cooked foods, spend in the temperature danger zone, the lower the chances of food poisoning.

High risk and perishable foods

No food will last forever, however well it is packaged and stored. High risk and perishable foods must be refrigerated because most food poisoning and spoilage bacteria do not multiply – or at least only multiply slowly – at 0°C–5°C. They include:

- raw meat, poultry and fish
- cooked meat, cooked poultry, fish and seafood
- products made from meat, poultry and fish, for example pies, pasties and pâtés.

Food storage and temperature chart

Food item	Storage method	Safety tips
Raw meat, poultry and game	Refrigerate (below 8°C), preferably with drip trays beneath	Store away from cooked meats to avoid cross contamination
Raw meat products, for example sausages, mince	Refrigerate (below 8°C)	Store away from cooked meats to avoid cross contamination
Bacon, whole cured ham	Refrigerate (below 8°C)	Store away from raw meat and meat products
Cooked meat and cooked meat products	Refrigerate (below 8°C)	Store away from raw meat and meat products Always store cooked meats, poultry, fish and ready-to-eat foods above raw foods
Fish (fresh)	Refrigerate (below 8°C), preferably in separate lidded compartments away from other foods which may become tainted	Keep no longer than one day
Fish (frozen)	Freezer (kept at −18°C)	Thaw only immediately before use
Fish (smoked or cured)	Refrigerate (below 8°C) away from other foods which may become tainted	
Fruit (fresh and dried)	Store in cool, dry, well-ventilated place away from other food at least 15 cm from ground	Throw away at the first sign of mould growth. Wash before serving or cooking.
Eggs	Refrigerate (below 8°C)	
Flour and cereals	Store in tightly lidded containers in dry, cool area	Use in date order
Fats, butter, margarine	Refrigerate (below 8°C)	Store away from highly flavoured food which may taint
Milk (fresh)	Refrigerate (below 8°C) in separate compartment and in strict rotation	Wipe sides and bottom of bottles with clean swab before refrigerating and again before removing cap. Throw it away if it has been damaged by birds
Prepared desserts, jellies, trifles, custards, creams, pastry cases, and so on	Refrigerate (below 8°C) if prepared more than 4 hours in advance	Should be prepared on day of use only
Soups, sauces, gravies, and so on	Refrigerate (below 8°C) if prepared more than 4 hours in advance	Should be prepared on day of use only
Bottled sauces without preservatives	Refrigerate (below 8°C)	Once open, refrigerate
Rice (uncooked), pasta (dried)	Store in a suitable lidded container	Keep dry
Rice (cooked), pasta (fresh)	Cook as near to time of use as possible. If it is to be used in a salad, chill quickly and refrigerate (below 8°C)	Do not reheat rice
Salad and fresh herbs	Refrigerate in chilled compartment	
Sugar, salt, bread	Store in tightly lidded bins in a cool, dry place	Wash thoroughly both before storage and before use
Canned goods (unopened)	Store in a cool, dry well-ventilated place	Do not use blown, dented, rusty or split tins
Bottled goods, for example jams, preserves	Store in a cool, dry well-ventilated place	Wipe bottles and jars with a clean swab before storing
Vegetables	Store in a cool, dry well-ventilated place	Use leaf vegetables on day of delivery or inspect frequently for deterioration

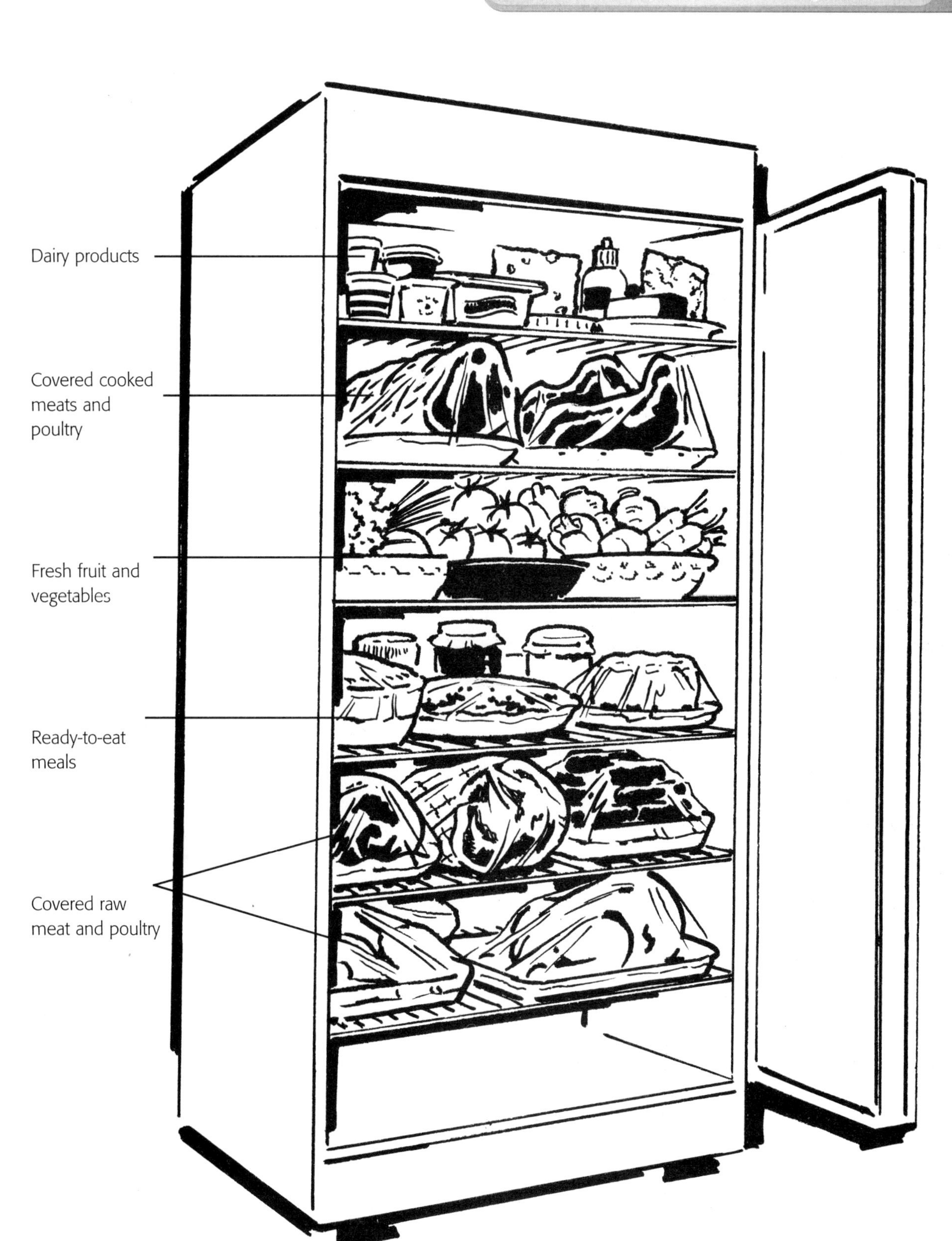

Correct storage of food in a fridge

Ten steps to safe storage in the fridge

1 Refrigerate foods immediately

- ❑ Put all meat and meat products, as well as dairy and other perishable items, into the fridge as soon as you take delivery.
- ❑ If there is food left over from preparation or serving which can be used later, it must be returned to the fridge immediately. Don't leave food in the temperature danger zone (8°C–63°C). Even a short time in this 'zone', which includes room temperature, can be extremely dangerous.
- ❑ It is essential that the fridge operates at the appropriate temperature, which for food refrigeration is 1°C–4°C. Freezers should be kept at –18°C or below. Make sure you have a reliable fridge thermometer.

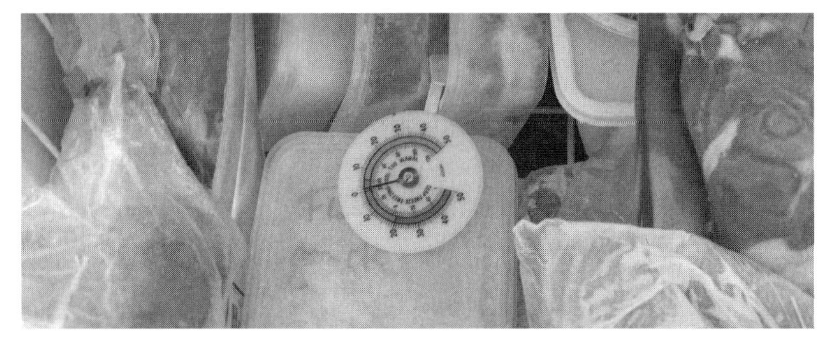

A fridge/freezer thermometer will help you to check that food is chilled to the correct temperature

2 Check temperature of incoming goods

- ❑ Always check the temperature of refrigerated and frozen food as it arrives. If the temperature is above safe storage levels, do not accept the delivery – the food could already be contaminated.

3 Maintain hygiene

- ❑ Keep all foods covered, especially meats.
- ❑ Clean the fridge regularly and mop up any spillage immediately.

4 Keep raw meats away from other foods

- ❑ Ideally, raw meats should be kept in a separate fridge, but if this is not possible uncooked foods should be kept in the lower part of the fridge below cooked foods. This is to avoid the dripping of juices which can cause dangerous contamination.

5 Store other products in the appropriate areas

- ❑ If the fridge has to be multi-purpose, keep non-dripping dairy products like cheese at the top of the cabinet, with cooked meats and meat products like pies and pâté below.
- ❑ Uncooked meats and sausages must be stored at the bottom of the fridge. If necessary, put red meats and sausages above uncooked poultry – but never the other way around.

6 Take care over salads

- ❑ Store salads below cooked meats but *always* above raw meats.
- ❑ Always keep salad covered, in a deep, lidded container or wrapped in cling film. Wash thoroughly before use.
- ❑ Note: In the home, salad is often stored at the bottom of the fridge, but this is not good food safety practice.

7 Rotate the stock

- ❑ Use labels or a dry-wipe board to record when foods are first placed in the fridge and make a note of use-by dates on packaging.
- ❑ Place newer stock at the back of the fridge to make sure items are used by the use-by date. Check each time you remove stock that it is within date.
- ❑ Ensure there is space between all items to allow airflow – this is essential for correct temperature to be maintained. Avoid standing food on the base of the fridge, and do not overload the fridge or it will not operate efficiently and safely.

8 When freezing, freeze immediately

- ❑ Pre-packed meat should always be used by the recommended date or frozen immediately.
- ❑ Follow the recommended storage times unless freezing meat immediately (see table on page 81).

9 Thaw thoroughly and safely

- ❑ *Note:* If you thaw food at room temperature you should check it regularly and put in into the fridge only when it is fully defrosted.
- ❑ Frozen meat must be thawed thoroughly before cooking or it will fail to cook properly. Either use a specially designed thaw cabinet, or thaw in a microwave.

- ❑ Liquid produced by thawing meat should be thrown away. Ensure that it does not drip on to other foods.
- ❑ Once frozen meat is thawed do not re-freeze unless it has been cooked first.

10 Once a package is opened, transfer to covered containers

- ❑ Once opened, always treat canned and packaged foods as fresh.
- ❑ Never store opened cans or other non-resealable packages in the fridge – instead transfer the contents to a covered container first.
- ❑ Wrapped and shrink-wrapped foods, including sliced meats and cheeses, should also be re-covered using cling film, foil or food-safe plastic containers as appropriate.
- ❑ Use food-grade cling film as low-grade cling films contain plasticides which will migrate into fatty foods such as cheese.

Keys to Good Practice: Safe refrigeration

- ✔ Throw out food which is going off.
- ✔ Store food you want to keep for a long time (or items like seafoods which are likely to spoil) in the coldest part of the fridge
- ✔ Cover all cooked foods and store them on a shelf *above* uncooked goods.
- ✔ Never put hot food in a fridge.
- ✔ Cool down hot foods to room temperature as quickly as possible before putting them in the fridge – and use within two days.
- ✔ Wrap foods with strong odours, such as seafoods and some cheeses.
- ✔ Avoid storing foods with strong odours near food such as milk and cream which may be tainted.
- ✔ Stack the shelves so that cold air can circulate, allowing you to check the contents and rotate the stock as necessary.
- ✔ Don't leave fridge doors open any longer than necessary.
- ✔ Use closed glass or plastic containers where possible, otherwise use cling film.

Recommended maximum storage times for meat

Type of meat	In a fridge
Uncooked:	
Joints of beef, pork and lamb	3 days
Steaks	2 days
Chops	2 days
Chicken (whole or portions)	2 days
Bacon rashers	7 days
Cubed meat	1 day
Minced meat	1 day
Liver, heart and kidneys	1 day
Sausages	3 days
Cooked:	
Joints	2 days
Chicken	2 days
Chicken, stuffed	2 days
Casseroles	2 days
Ham	2 days
Meat pies	1 day
Sliced meat	2 days
Pâté	2 days

Storage of frozen food

A freezer should run at –18°C or cooler (large commercial freezers operate at lower temperatures). In a freezer bacterial growth should stop completely. Some bacteria may even be killed if frozen so freezing is a good option for storing foods for long periods of time. However, some spores and pathogens can survive freezing and if the temperature rises above –10°C, spoilage organisms (moulds and yeasts) may start to grow.

Frozen food should never be re-frozen once it has thawed or partly defrosted because the food may have been sufficiently warm for long enough to allow pathogenic bacteria to multiply.

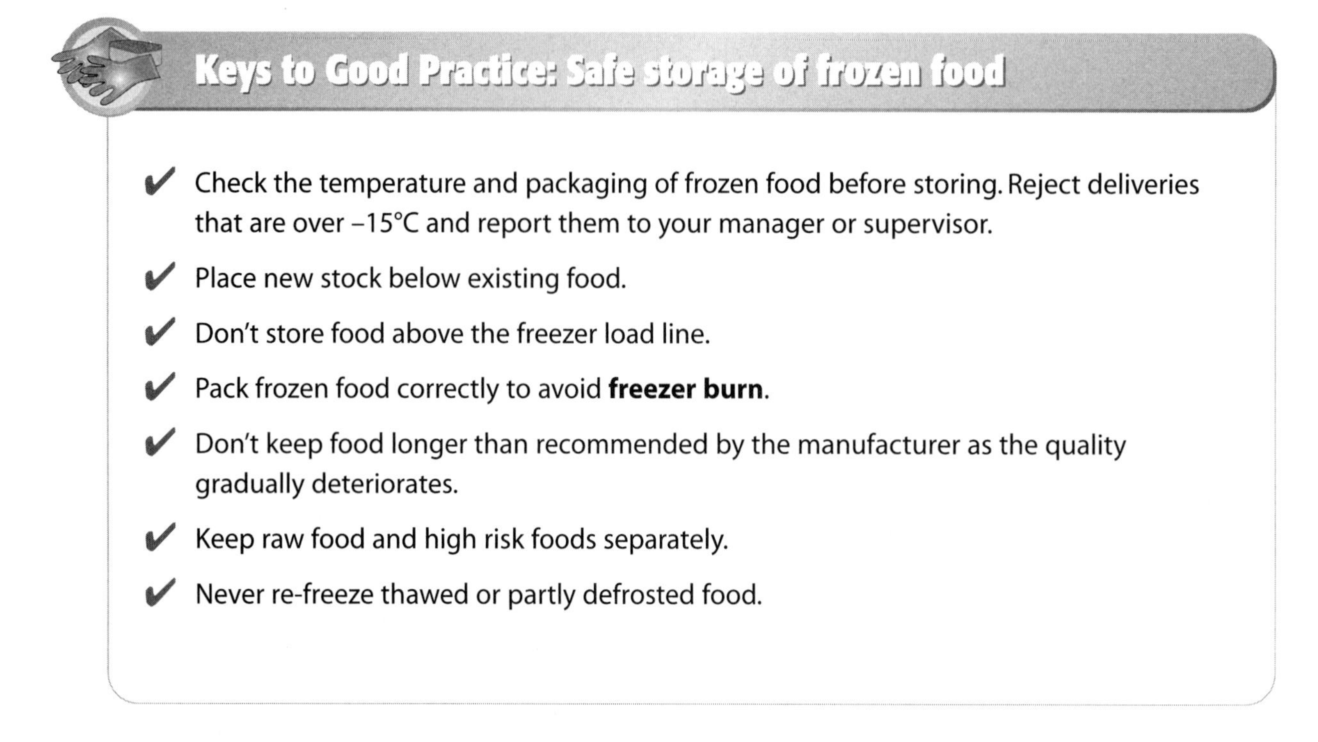

Keys to Good Practice: Safe storage of frozen food

- ✔ Check the temperature and packaging of frozen food before storing. Reject deliveries that are over –15°C and report them to your manager or supervisor.
- ✔ Place new stock below existing food.
- ✔ Don't store food above the freezer load line.
- ✔ Pack frozen food correctly to avoid **freezer burn**.
- ✔ Don't keep food longer than recommended by the manufacturer as the quality gradually deteriorates.
- ✔ Keep raw food and high risk foods separately.
- ✔ Never re-freeze thawed or partly defrosted food.

Freezer storage times

Always check the label on pre-packed food to see if it is suitable for home freezing. If so, freeze as soon as possible after purchase. The star marking panel on food labels will tell you how long you can store food, depending on the type of freezer.

When freezing home-cooked foods, use clean freezer bags and label them with the date and a description of the food. Again, check the freezer manual or cook book to see how long you can store the foods.

Remember, use up older items first – *first in, first out* – and if in doubt throw it out.

Maintaining the fridge and freezer

Use a thermometer to check fridge and freezer temperatures. The coldest part of the fridge should be at no more than 8°C and the freezer at –18°C or below.

Avoid overloading. If a fridge is over-packed with food or is iced up, it is harder to keep the temperature down. Never place food in front of the cooling unit.

Clean all internal and external surfaces regularly, especially fridge shelves and door storage compartments. Mop up any spills as soon as they happen.

Defrost the fridge/freezer regularly. Most fridges and some freezers automatically defrost; check the guidance supplied with the equipment to see if, and how often, de-frosting should be carried out.

Safe storage of hot food

Keys to Good Practice: Keeping cooked food hot

- ✔ Heat food so that the core temperature is at least 75°C before being placed in a heated cabinet or trolley – use a food thermometer if necessary, ensuring that the probe does not touch the base of the heated trays.
- ✔ Don't use warmers or heated food cabinets for heating or re-heating. Use only for holding food that is *already* hot (above 63°C).
- ✔ Bring food warmers and cabinets to the required temperature before use.
- ✔ Check the food and set the thermostat of the equipment to maintain the correct temperature.
- ✔ Keep food in a heated cabinet for a maximum of one hour.
- ✔ Don't stack food above the level of the trays or else it will not remain hot enough and will fall into the temperature danger zone (8°C–63°C).

Preservation of food

There are various methods of preserving food. They all aim:

- to extend the shelf life of food
- to destroy or delay the spoilage organisms which can make food unfit to eat.

Food **preservation** usually makes food safer to eat. Food factories are able to use highly processed foods to cut down production time and to remove the risks of food poisoning. One example is the use of reconstituted spray-dried eggs in the mass production of cakes and custards. Cracking open hundreds of eggs, which are a high risk food, would be both unhygienic and time consuming. Reconstituted eggs have been heat treated and are free from pathogenic bacteria.

Methods of food preservation

The methods used vary according to the type of food. Often a combination of techniques is used, for example vacuum packing followed by refrigeration. The main ones are described below:

- **Drying** (dehydrating) – removing most of the water from food. *Examples*: meat, soups, fish, stocks, tea, coffee. *Why it works*: bacteria need water to multiply, so removing water stops the growth of pathogenic and food spoilage bacteria.
- **The use of low temperatures** – freezing and refrigeration of perishable foods. *Examples:* all perishable foods – fresh meat, fish, vegetables, fruit, and so on. *Why it works*: bacteria need warmth to multiply; temperatures below 5°C are not in the temperature danger zone where bacteria can flourish.
- **Chemical preservation** – pickling, salting, sugaring and curing food. *Examples:* fish, meat, fruit, vegetables, jam. *Why it works:* the preservations ensure no water is available for bacteria to multiply with.
- **Heat treatment** – sterilising food and drink by heating it to a very high temperature. *Examples:* canning, bottling, cooking, pasteurisation and Ultra Heat Treatment (UHT) of a wide range of foods and drinks. *Why it works:* extreme heat applied for a long enough time will kill all bacteria.
- **Vacuum packing and sealing** – removing air from packets of food. *Examples:* meat, poultry, fish and some vegetables. *Why it works:* most food poisoning bacteria cannot multiply without oxygen, although there are some that can.

Some of these processes, particularly those using extreme heat, may alter the taste of the food. Two other processes which affect the quality of the food we eat are irradiation and GM foods.

Food irradiation

Food irradiation is a processing and preservation method. Food is exposed to electron beams, X-rays or gamma rays which:

- produce a similar effect to pasteurisation, cooking or other forms of heat treatment, but does not have as much effect on look and texture
- can be used to kill bacteria which cause food poisoning such as salmonella, campylobacter and E. coli
- can delay fruit ripening and help stop vegetables such as potatoes and onions from sprouting.

Is food irradiation safe? The **Food Standards Agency** says that decades of research worldwide have shown that irradiation of food is a safe and effective way to kill bacteria in foods and extend their shelf life. In the UK, only correctly labelled irradiated herbs, spices or vegetable seasonings are permitted, although national regulations do allow for the irradiation of seven categories of food: fruit, vegetables, cereals, bulbs and tubers, spices and condiments, fish and shellfish and poultry. The Food Standards Agency believes that irradiation is a matter of consumer choice rather than a food safety issue.

Genetically modified (GM) foods

Genetic modification is the method of changing the genetic make-up of an individual organism by inserting, removing or altering individual genes to achieve a particular result. Take the tomato, for example. It is used in lots of foods. GM tomatoes have been produced to last longer, look redder and taste better. Traditionally, plants have been improved by breeding them with other, better plants – a natural process which takes years. But with GM foods this is done quickly and artificially in a laboratory. The whole issue of genetic modification has become highly controversial.

GM crops are being grown on a few farms in Britain as an experiment, but many people have become so worried about GM foods that most of the big supermarkets have banned them.

The arguments for and against GM foods

For	Against
Plants can be bred to fight off weeds and pests, so crops are never spoiled	GM foods can damage your health – research has shown that rats eating them did not grow properly
More food can be produced, like rice, to feed the world's starving people	New diseases could be created by accident
Food may become cheaper because there would be more of it	Different species are being mixed up, for example to give a tomato a more reddish colour it may be given parts of a very red fish, which seems to be against nature
There have already been great advances in genetic modification in medicine (see below) – there could be similar advances in foods	Because GM foods are new, there has not been any long-term testing to see if they are dangerous to humans

In medicine, GM technology is widely used to produce products that were once obtained from either human tissue or animal tissue. Haemophiliacs, for example, no longer face the risk of infection from contaminated blood products because GM technology has been used to produce blood products that are identical to those coming from natural sources.

Stock rotation

All stock in food premises should be routinely rotated. Stock rotation involves using a product with the shortest shelf life before using a similar product with a longer shelf life. The golden rule is: 'first in, first out'. This is important for the following reasons:

- it ensures that older food is used first
- it helps avoid spoilage
- it ensures that food is of good quality and safe to eat
- it helps to maintain the correct levels of stock
- it reduces the risk of insect and rodent infestations.

Checks should be made daily on **perishable** food stored in the fridge. Weekly checks should be sufficient for other foods.

Labelling on food

Date marks

In most countries food must be labelled (by law) with a date showing the period when the food is safe to eat. Date marks must appear on most packaged food. The two most important date marks are:

- **use-by date**
- **best-before date**

Use-by date

This mark is found on highly perishable packaged food – those that 'go off' quite quickly such as:

- cooked meats
- chilled ham
- sausages
- fish and dairy products.

The **use-by date** means that the food has a short shelf life and could become a health risk if stored incorrectly or for too long. Any food that is past the use-by date is likely to be unfit to eat, even if it looks and smells fine.

Best-before date

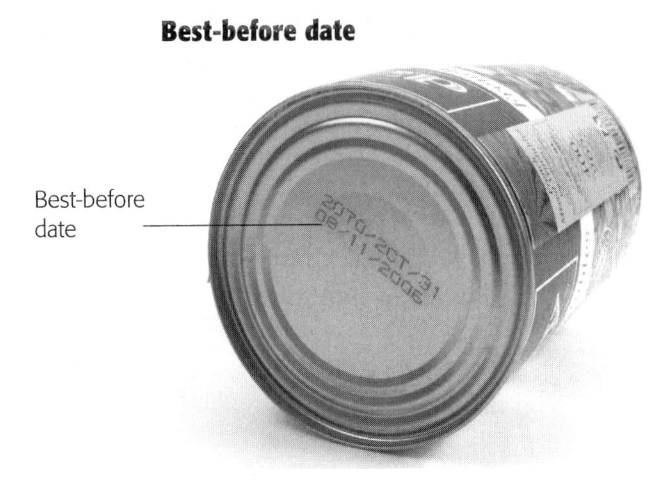

This is used for food that can safely be kept for longer. It is found on:

- frozen foods
- dried fruit
- flour, cakes and cereals
- canned food.

If eaten by the **best-before date**, you can be confident that the food is at its best quality. Eating food after that date may not be dangerous but it probably won't taste or smell as good.

Display-until mark

Supermarkets also use display-until date marks. This helps them to plan their stock rotation, that is, making sure that the oldest products are displayed at the front of the shelf and therefore sold first.

Storage and cooking instructions

Packaged foods also have to display a storage instructions label. It is important to take notice of these instructions as some less obvious foods – bottled sauces and preserves, for example – should be stored in the fridge once opened.

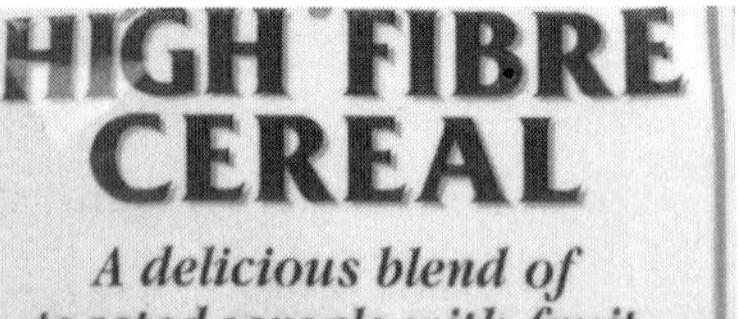

Storage instructions label

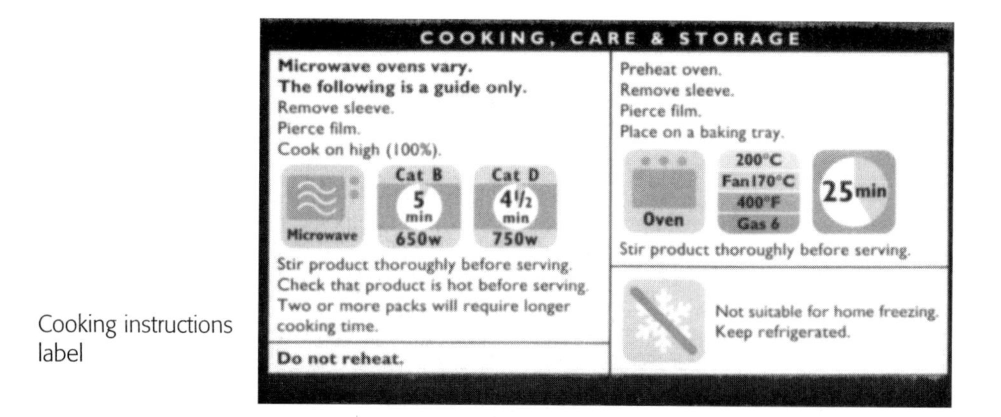

Cooking instructions label

Protecting food from airborne hazards

Air and dust carry millions of microscopic particles of dead skin. Food left out before serving should be kept covered at all times. Other hazards include flies – blue- and green-bottles – all of which contaminate food by directly landing on it and by dropping their eggs and faeces.

Activity: True or false

Decide which of the statements below are true and which are false.

1. Refrigeration prevents bacterial growth.
2. The fridge temperature should be set at below 8°C and the freezer temperature should be set at –18°C.
3. The best method to thaw food is at room temperature.
4. The fridge should be tightly packed with food and containers to keep items cold.
5. A fridge/freezer thermometer is the best tool to check and monitor the temperature inside the fridge and freezer compartments.
6. Perishables, prepared foods and leftovers need to be refrigerated or frozen within four hours of purchase or preparation.
7. To thaw food quickly, submerge it in cold water in airtight packaging or thaw in the microwave and cook immediately.
8. Always marinate foods in the fridge.
9. When travelling put perishable food in a cool bag in the boot to avoid sunlight and added heat.

(Answers on page 179.)

Knowledge Test

Choose the correct answer in each case.

1 Best-before dates on food indicate:

- **a** the time until which the food is in its best condition
- **b** when it is safe to eat the food
- **c** the date by which the food must be sold
- **d** when the food was produced.

2 Use-by dates are shown on food that:

- **a** needs to be stored in a freezer
- **b** is in the high risk category
- **c** is highly perishable
- **d** must be cooked thoroughly.

3 Which of these is specific enough to be a use-by date?

- **a** March 2004
- **b** 3/2004
- **c** 7 March

4 In addition to the cooking instructions, what other labelling information must be followed to ensure that you know the food is safe to eat?

- **a** Ingredients list
- **b** Nutrition information
- **c** Storage instructions

5 Date marks are used by food manufacturers to help maintain food quality. They are also used:

- **a** to help prevent food poisoning
- **b** to speed up food distribution to supermarkets
- **c** to allow them to reduce the price when the date has passed.

Knowledge Test

6 Which of the following foods should have a use-by date, not a best-before date?

a Packet of biscuits
b Fresh chilled ready-to-eat-meal
c Bottled cola drink

7 What is the principle called by which food that is oldest is sold first?

a Crop rotation
b Stock rotation
agement

fridge should raw meat be stored, and why?

est part of the fridge so that it keeps fresh for longer.

tom shelf of the fridge so that it does not taint
s.

tom shelf of the fridge away from cooked meat to avoid cross contamination from dripping juices.

d On the top shelf of the fridge so that it may be easily observed for freshness.

9 Which of the following temperatures is in the temperature danger zone?

a 3°C
b 35°C
c 65°C
d 95°C

10 Once the date stamped on a milk carton has been reached, the milk:

a should not be sold
b should not be used
c has lost most of its nutritional value
d all of the above.

(Answers on page 180.)

Chapter 7

Food preparation and cooking

So, the food in your workplace has been correctly stored and is fresh and good to eat. The next step is to prepare and cook it correctly and safely. It goes without saying that the food areas must be spotlessly clean and disinfected (see Chapter 9). This chapter looks at the actual preparation of meals. In Chapter 3 you learned which categories of food carry a high risk of food poisoning. Many of these risks can be avoided by cooking the food correctly – for long enough and at the right temperature.

Topics covered in this chapter include:

- ❑ **Cooking to correct temperatures and times.**
- ❑ **Cooling hot food safely.**
- ❑ **Recognising high risk foods.**
- ❑ **Reheating of foods.**
- ❑ **Using microwave ovens for cooking and reheating.**
- ❑ **Thawing food.**
- ❑ **Hygienic food preparation.**

Cooking to correct temperatures and times

Food is cooked properly when it has been heated for a long enough time and at a high enough temperature to kill the bacteria which cause food poisoning. As a rough guide, most bacteria are destroyed at temperatures of 70°C or hotter once the **core temperature** – the temperature at the centre of the food – has been kept at this temperature for at least two minutes.

Safety tip!

The best way to destroy bacteria found in food is to cook it.

You can check the temperature inside the food using a food thermometer. This is important because although the surface of the food may be cooked, the centre of the food could still be in the **temperature danger zone**.

Quick fact

The temperature danger zone is 8°C–63°C. This is the temperature range in which food poisoning bacteria may grow.

A food thermometer

Cold food (which is to be served hot) will need to be quickly and thoroughly heated until it is piping hot and then kept hot until it is served. It is best to reheat the food to a temperature of at least 82°C and hold the food at this temperature for at least two minutes.

Wherever possible, cook food close to the time that it will be eaten. This reduces the chance of the food becoming contaminated after it has been cooked. It also means that there won't be enough time for food poisoning bacteria to grow to dangerous levels on the cooked food before it is eaten.

Cooking meat

- **Steaks**. There is always a risk of food poisoning when eating beef or lamb steaks, not on the bone, that has been cooked (fried or grilled) rare, that is, so the middle is pinkish, not well done. The outside needs to be thoroughly cooked to kill any germs on the surface of the meat. However this is an 'acceptable' risk for healthy adults, but not for the risk groups (e.g. the elderly or those in hospital).
- **Chicken, joints of meat on the bone**. Whichever cooking method you use – frying, grilling, roasting or microwaving – chicken and meat must be cooked right through on the bone. There should be no pink bits in the middle.
- **Meat products, for example sausages, burgers and mince**. These must be cooked right through to the middle. When frying burgers the temperature on the outside may get up to 170°C in minutes, but the centre may still only be at 65°C in the centre.

Keys to Good Practice: Cooking and heating food safely

- ✔ Follow recipes and label instructions on cooking times and correct temperatures.
- ✔ Always preheat the oven properly.
- ✔ Always cook food thoroughly – until it is piping hot (75°C).
- ✔ Use a food thermometer to check the centre of cooked foods, especially meat and poultry (75°C).
- ✔ Stir casseroles and stews regularly during cooking to make sure there are no cool spots.
- ✔ Cook chicken, sausages and hamburgers until juices run clear and there are no pink bits in the middle.
- ✔ Make sure the outside of lamb and beef steaks are thoroughly cooked.
- ✔ Don't partially cook food and then warm it up later.
- ✔ Cook eggs until the white and yolk are firm (see Chapter 4, page 53).
- ✔ Cook food as close as possible to the time that it is to be eaten.
- ✔ Once cooked, keep foods covered and piping hot until it is time to eat them – use a special warming food cabinet set to the right temperature.
- ✔ Quickly and thoroughly reheat cold food which is to be served hot (to 82°C).

Cooling hot food safely

In Chapter 2 you read about food poisoning bacteria that can protect themselves from high temperatures during cooking by forming spores (see page 21). While they will not be present in enough numbers to make someone sick just after the food is cooked, they *can* start growing again if the cooked food is left in the temperature danger zone. This is why cooling cooked food quickly is very important.

Hot food passes through the temperature danger zone as it cools, so you need to reduce its temperature as quickly as possible. If food is to be pre-cooked and then cooled, it will need to be cooled *rapidly* to 5°C. If a large container of cooked food, for example a beef curry, is placed in a fridge for cooling, it can take as long as 24 hours to cool to 5°C. This is very dangerous as the centre of the food will remain warm and allow food poisoning bacteria to grow.

Safety tip!

Cooked food should be cooled to 5°C within 6 hours:

Cool from 60°C to 21°C within 2 hours, and from 21°C to 5°C within a further 4 hours.

To speed cooling it is a good idea to divide foods into smaller portions, place them in a wide dish and stand this in a shallow tray of cold water. The larger surface area helps to speed up the cooling process.

However, you should never put steaming hot food straight into the fridge because the fridge temperature will rise, causing condensation which can contaminate other foods.

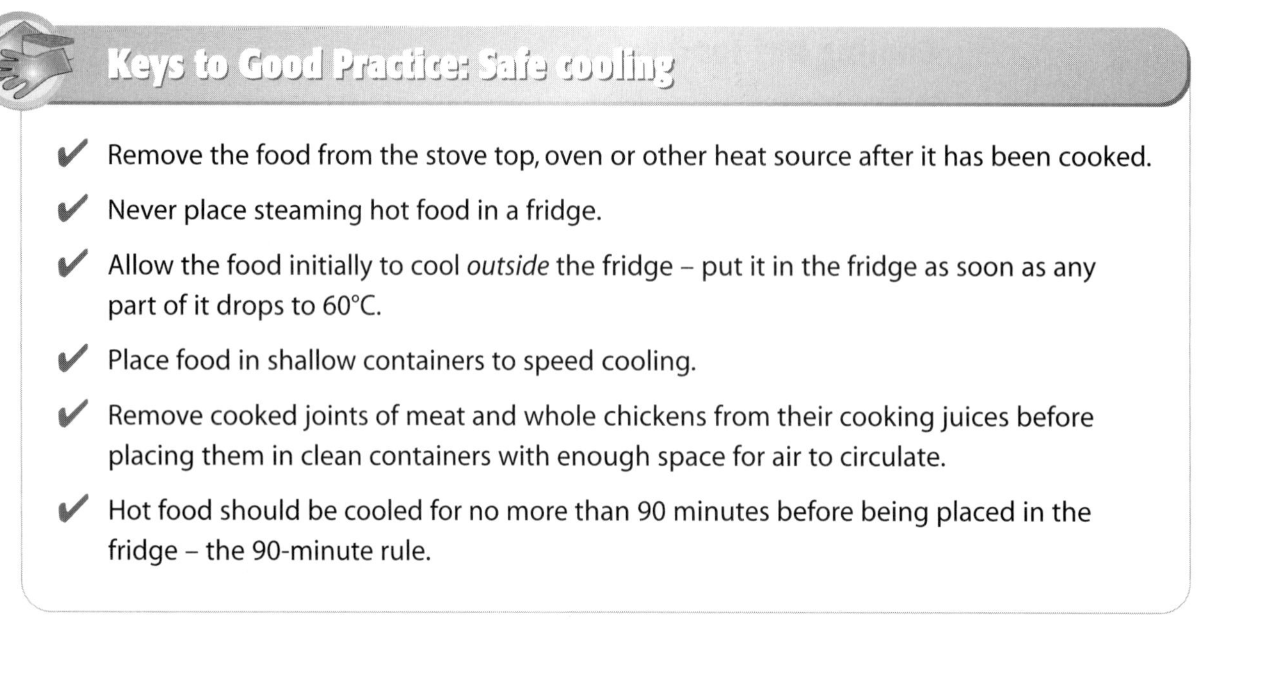

Keys to Good Practice: Safe cooling

- ✔ Remove the food from the stove top, oven or other heat source after it has been cooked.
- ✔ Never place steaming hot food in a fridge.
- ✔ Allow the food initially to cool *outside* the fridge – put it in the fridge as soon as any part of it drops to 60°C.
- ✔ Place food in shallow containers to speed cooling.
- ✔ Remove cooked joints of meat and whole chickens from their cooking juices before placing them in clean containers with enough space for air to circulate.
- ✔ Hot food should be cooled for no more than 90 minutes before being placed in the fridge – the 90-minute rule.

Recognising high risk foods

High risk foods are foods which provide ideal conditions for pathogenic (harmful) bacteria to grow and multiply. These were described in Chapters 2 and 3 and include:

- meat
- poultry
- milk, cream and cheese
- fish, shellfish
- eggs
- cooked rice and pasta
- fruit and vegetables
- food that is grown on or near the ground
- all products made from these foods – sauces, cakes, soups, and so on.

Some of these foods (raw meat, for example) naturally contain small numbers of pathogenic bacteria and provide ideal conditions for bacterial growth. However, they do not pose a food poisoning risk as long as you cook the item thoroughly to destroy the bacteria.

Ready-to-eat foods

Ready-to-eat foods – which are likely to be stored in the fridge and then reheated by the consumer – are the most hazardous of all the high risk foods:

- They provide good conditions for bacterial growth – food, moisture, warmth, oxygen and a neutral **pH** (acidity) level.
- The food is not cooked immediately before eating (which would kill the bacteria).

Examples of high risk foods are:

- cooked meat and cooked poultry
- cooked food containing meat or poultry, for example stews, casseroles, lasagne, soups made with meat stock
- meat or fish pâtés or pastes
- dairy products, for example milk, custard and dairy-based desserts such as cheesecakes and cream cakes
- seafood and shellfish, including scampi, lobster, prawns, shrimps, mussels and crab – includes seafood salad, fish stews and stocks
- cooked rice and pasta
- dishes containing eggs which are either uncooked (as in home-made mayonnaise) or undercooked (as in mousses).

Ready-to-eat meals

Reheating of foods

Food poisoning bacteria will start to multiply when chilled food is reheated to temperatures above 8°C (the temperature danger zone) and will stop multiplying when the food reaches 63°C. The longer it takes for food to reheat to 63°C, the greater the number of bacteria that may be in the food.

The recommended maximum time to reheat food is *2 hours*. The food must reach at least 82°C for a minimum of 3 minutes.

Keys to Good Practice: Safe heating of food

- ✔ Reheat food rapidly.
- ✔ Heat food to at least 82°C.
- ✔ Don't reheat food for more than 2 hours.
- ✔ Never reheat food more than once and throw away leftovers.
- ✔ Keep hot food at 63°C or above until it is eaten.

Using microwave ovens for cooking and reheating

Microwaves do not always cook food evenly and there may be cold spots where bacteria and viruses survive. When using a microwave oven you will need to check that the food has been cooked all the way through. Use a food thermometer at the end of standing time to do this.

Many products come with microwave cooking instructions and it is important to follow them. You will need to know what wattage your microwave operates at because less powerful microwaves will need more cooking time than higher powered ones.

If you look after babies it is best not to heat bottles containing milk or formula in the microwave. A touch test may not reveal how hot some parts of the milk are and the baby's mouth could be scalded.

Keys to Good Practice: Safe use of microwave ovens

- ✔ Always follow the product's microwave cooking instructions – check out the wattage of your microwave oven.
- ✔ Arrange food items evenly in a covered dish and add some liquid if needed. Cover the dish with a lid or plastic wrap – loosen or vent the lid or wrap to let steam escape. The moist heat that is created will help destroy harmful bacteria and ensure uniform cooking. Cooking bags also provide safe, even cooking.
- ✔ When partially cooking food in a microwave oven to finish cooking on a grill or in a conventional oven, transfer the microwaved food to the other heat source immediately.
- ✔ Never partially cook food and store it for later use.
- ✔ Stir food and turn large items over during cooking. Rotate the dish once or twice – even if you have a rotating turntable.
- ✔ Cut food into similar sized pieces, or arrange thicker pieces on the outside of the dish.
- ✔ Make sure that food is steaming throughout and not just at the edges.
- ✔ Food continues to cook when the oven is turned off. Always wait 3–5 minutes, or for the recommended standing time, before testing that cooking is complete.
- ✔ Don't heat baby's bottles in the microwave.

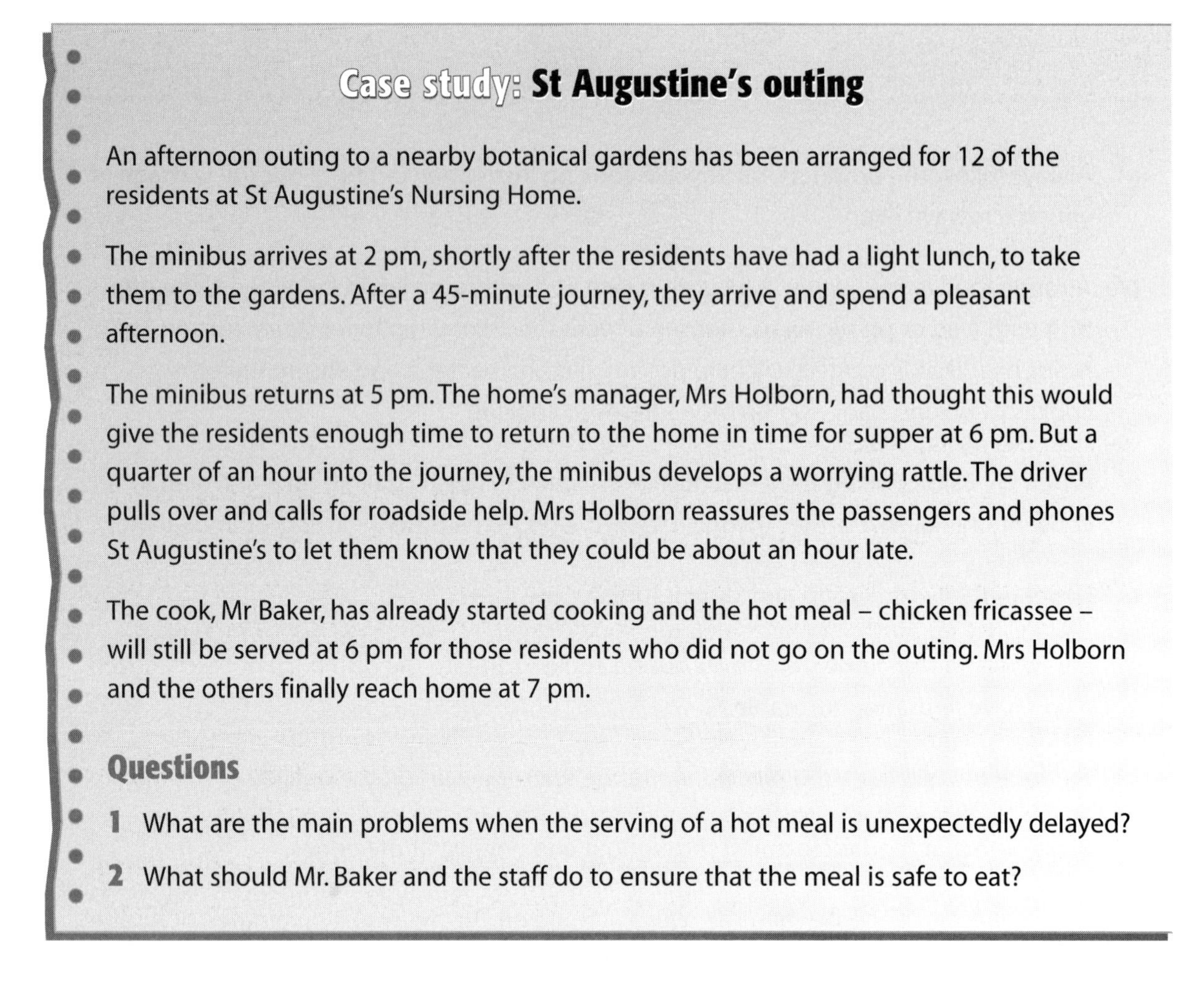

Case study: St Augustine's outing

An afternoon outing to a nearby botanical gardens has been arranged for 12 of the residents at St Augustine's Nursing Home.

The minibus arrives at 2 pm, shortly after the residents have had a light lunch, to take them to the gardens. After a 45-minute journey, they arrive and spend a pleasant afternoon.

The minibus returns at 5 pm. The home's manager, Mrs Holborn, had thought this would give the residents enough time to return to the home in time for supper at 6 pm. But a quarter of an hour into the journey, the minibus develops a worrying rattle. The driver pulls over and calls for roadside help. Mrs Holborn reassures the passengers and phones St Augustine's to let them know that they could be about an hour late.

The cook, Mr Baker, has already started cooking and the hot meal – chicken fricassee – will still be served at 6 pm for those residents who did not go on the outing. Mrs Holborn and the others finally reach home at 7 pm.

Questions

1 What are the main problems when the serving of a hot meal is unexpectedly delayed?

2 What should Mr. Baker and the staff do to ensure that the meal is safe to eat?

Thawing food

Some foods such as ready-to-eat meals, frozen vegetables and pies can be cooked from frozen. Most raw frozen foods like meat and poultry must be completely thawed before cooking. Inadequate thawing often causes food poisoning because the food is kept in the temperature danger zone.

Keys to Good Practice: Thawing food safely

- ✔ Always follow the manufacturer's instructions for thawing.
- ✔ Thaw food in a specially designed thawing cabinet at temperatures between 10°C and 15°C.
- ✔ Always carry out thawing in an area entirely separate from other foods – to avoid risk of contamination from thawed liquid.
- ✔ Always allow sufficient time for thawing.
- ✔ Never re-freeze food once it has started to thaw.
- ✔ Only thaw food in a microwave oven if it is to be cooked immediately; and follow the instructions that came with the microwave because of the risk of uneven heating.
- ✔ Place the food in a container that will hold the thawing juices – to prevent overflowing and dripping. Wash the container and your hands thoroughly after use as the juices could be contaminated.
- ✔ Cover the food to prevent contamination.
- ✔ If using a multi-purpose fridge for thawing, always place frozen raw food on the lowest shelf to prevent juices dripping on to other foods and contaminating them.
- ✔ To thaw very large turkeys and so on more quickly, let them defrost outside the fridge. Put them in a cool place (covered) and make sure they are completely thawed before cooking.
- ✔ Never re-freeze thawed food.

Thawing and cooking times for frozen poultry

Oven-ready weight (in kg)	Approximate number of hours needed for thawing at room temperature	Minimum number of hours needed for cooking in foil at 180°C
2.25	15	2.5
4.50	18	3.5
6.75	24	4.75
9.00	30	5.75

Hygienic food preparation

The main hazards (risks) when preparing food are:

- cross contamination
- multiplying bacteria.

Both carry a serious risk of food poisoning.

There are four basic rules to follow to make sure that the food you prepare is safe and hygienic:

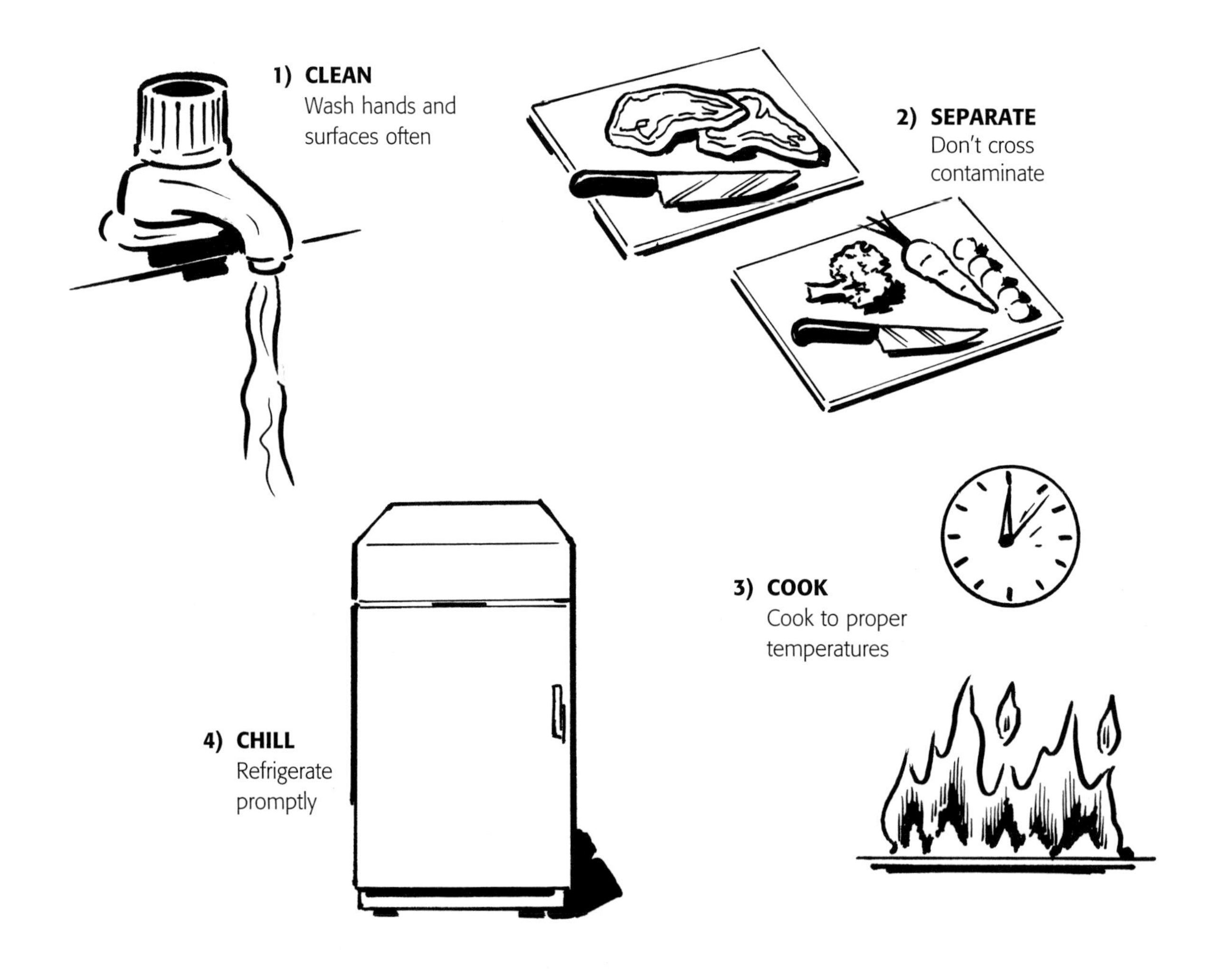

Safety tip!

If wearing gloves wear them for one task only, for example slicing ham for sandwiches. When you start the next task wear new gloves – and remember to wash your hands too.

1 Clean

Be clean yourself

Bacteria can be present throughout the kitchen so you will need to be very clean.

Wash your hands thoroughly with hot soapy water frequently, but always:

- before handling food
- after handling raw meat, poultry or fish
- after using the toilet
- after gardening or handling rubbish
- after handling a pet or other animal
- after smoking
- after sneezing or coughing.

Keep the work area clean

Wash surfaces and utensils *frequently*. After preparing each food item and before you go on to the next food, you should always clean:

- all preparation and eating surfaces using hot soapy water
- chopping boards, knives and other utensils
- cloths and towels if not using single-use cloths.

Wash raw fruit and vegetables

Raw fruit and vegetables should be washed in cold running water.

2 Separate

Prevent cross contamination

Cross contamination is when ready-to-eat food is contaminated with bacteria:

- *directly* by contact with raw meat, poultry, fish or unwashed vegetables
- *indirectly* by contact with hands, utensils or work surfaces that harbour harmful bacteria.

To prevent cross contamination you need to take these precautions:

- Always store raw meat by itself on the bottom shelf or in the drawer of the fridge so that juices cannot drip on to other food.
- Never place other food in direct contact with raw meat, poultry, fish or unwashed vegetables.
- Pack raw meat, poultry and fish separately at the supermarket. Make sure other meat products such as cooked ham are never packed in the same bag.
- Use a different cutting board and utensils for raw meat products.
- Always wash hands, cutting boards, utensils and dishes after they come into contact with raw meat, poultry, eggs, seafood and unwashed fruit and vegetables.

3 Cook

Cook to proper temperatures

Foods are cooked properly when they are heated to a high enough temperature and for a long enough time to kill the harmful bacteria which cause food poisoning. To be safe, follow these precautions:

- Follow a recipe or the cooking advice label on the packet.
- Always cook food to a high temperature for the right amount of time to kill any bacteria. Food should be cooked to a core temperature of 75°C.
- Buy and use a meat thermometer. If you don't have one, be sure to cook burgers, chicken and pork until the juices run clear.

- If you are reheating food, such as a fish pie, only do it once. Make sure you reheat to piping hot (82°C) to kill any bacteria that have survived in the food during cooling and refrigeration.
- Never pour hot gravy or sauce on to cold food.

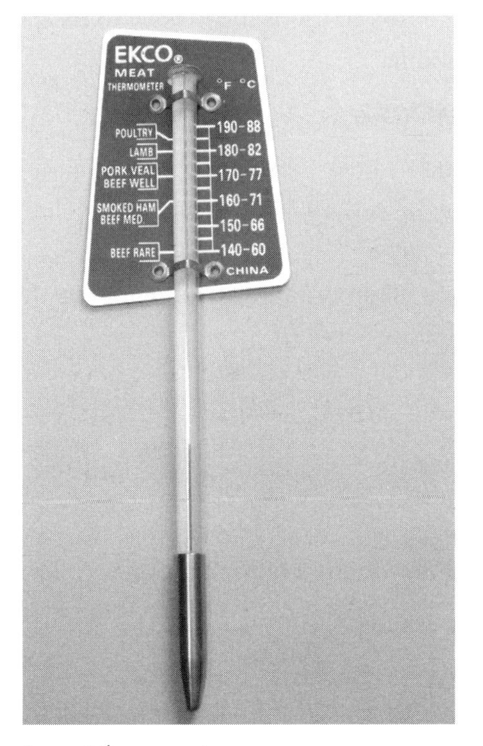

A meat thermometer

4 Chill

Refrigerate foods quickly

The reason we refrigerate foods such as meats, dairy products and certain vegetables and fruits is that most bacteria do not multiply below 6°C. The correct temperature for a fridge is between zero and 5°C. At this temperature the food remains ready for cooking or eating. For this reason, you need to:

- store chilled foods in the fridge immediately after you return from shopping
- refrigerate **perishable** foods as soon as possible after cooking
- chill or freeze cooked food in shallow pans to allow quick cooling
- allow plenty of time to thaw frozen meat and poultry – following the guidelines on page 101.

Knowledge Test

Choose the right answer in each case.

1 We call the category of foods most likely to be a source of food poisoning bacteria:

- **a** ready-to-eat foods
- **b** low risk foods
- **c** high risk foods.

2 What is the safe minimum temperature for keeping food hot after cooking and before serving?

- **a** 63°C
- **b** 75°C
- **c** 55°C

3 Which of the following is a high risk food?

- **a** Flour
- **b** Raw chicken
- **c** Sliced ham

4 Which is the safest way to defrost a frozen chicken to be eaten for Sunday lunch?

- **a** Place in a bowl of lukewarm water as soon as you get up on Sunday morning.
- **b** Defrost in the microwave the night before, then chill.
- **c** Place in the fridge 24 hours before cooking.

5 If you bought a ready-made meal from the supermarket, how would you know how to cook it?

- **a** Look in a cookery book.
- **b** Follow the preparation instructions on the label.
- **c** Put it in the microwave for at least four minutes on full power.

Knowledge Test

6 Which is the most common error that can lead to food poisoning?

a Not using the food by the use-by date.

b Not cooking food properly.

c Not disinfecting food preparation surfaces.

7 Which of the following is an example of food poisoning?

a Sickness 24 hours after eating reheated risotto.

b Headache and nausea the morning after a party where 'corked' wine of poor quality has been served.

c Vomiting and a skin rash after eating an instant packet soup.

8 Which of the following is an example of food that contains food poisoning bacteria?

a Fresh, opened meat turning a brown colour.

b A cut apple going brown.

c Lettuce leaves wilting.

d Bread going stale.

e None of the above.

(Answers on pages 180–1.)

Chapter 8

Delivering food to clients, serving and handling

Eating and drinking is one of the most enjoyable parts of our lives. It is particularly important that those receiving care are given the opportunity, as far as is practical, to enjoy their meals when and where they want to. Mealtimes are also important social occasions and are often used to mark special occasions and to celebrate particular cultural customs. For many of us, *where* we eat plays a large part in our enjoyment of *what* we eat. Time is another important factor – it is important that mealtimes remain as unhurried and unstressful as possible.

People who need care may need special diets or they may need assistance with eating and drinking. This could result in a loss of dignity and independence unless assistance is offered in a well thought out way – one which recognises the importance of maintaining freedom of choice and independence for every individual.

This chapter looks at the ways in which you can help to make mealtimes enjoyable and safe for your clients. It covers the following topics:

- ❑ **Preparing food in a care environment.**
- ❑ **Preparing for mealtimes.**
- ❑ **Serving food.**
- ❑ **Helping people with special needs to eat and drink.**
- ❑ **Helping clients with shopping and cooking.**
- ❑ **Special occasions – making sandwiches, barbecues and picnics.**

Preparing food in a care environment

Your job may or may not include preparing food for clients. For example, if you work in a day centre you may need to make only hot drinks. If you work in a residential care home, hospital or nursing home, the cooking will be done centrally and your task will be to serve the food and drinks to clients at the appropriate times.

When preparing or serving food, it is important to remember the key principles of care:

- Respect the individual, their customs and beliefs.
- Promote freedom of choice.
- Communicate effectively with clients.

Keys to Good Practice: Helping people to eat and drink

- ✔ Know each client's individual dietary needs and any special dietary customs, for example diabetic, vegetarian, or **halal** diets.
- ✔ Find out what the individual's personal likes and dislikes are by discussing choices with them; then record these for other staff to see.
- ✔ If there are any specific problems with eating, make sure that the appropriate utensils are available and offer assistance when necessary.
- ✔ Make sure that clients know what is available for them and, if necessary, help them to make a choice.
- ✔ Discuss where and when the client prefers to eat and, whenever possible, try to meet their needs.
- ✔ Provide a relaxing and comfortable environment in which to enjoy meals.

Preparing for mealtimes

Once you have found out where clients would like to eat, they should be given the opportunity to:

- go to the toilet
- wash their hands.

If the client wears dentures, check that these are comfortably in place. Some people find it uncomfortable to sit at a table to eat their meals. Instead, they should be offered an alternative, such as eating from a tray on their lap. Provide a napkin or other suitable protection for their clothes.

The eating area should be prepared too. Make sure that all the crockery and cutlery is clean and that each person has space to eat comfortably and to reach their glass of water or juice.

Pay special attention to the social side of mealtimes:

- Make sure the client is in a comfortable position for eating – at the right height and distance from the table.
- Arrange the seating so that people can see and talk to each other during the meal. For some people in day centres and residential care, mealtimes may be their only opportunity to socialise.

Serving food

The way food is served is very important and is part of the caring values of the care setting:

- Arranging food on the plate so that it looks tempting will encourage the client to eat.
- Food should be hot, but not so hot that it could scald the client's mouth.
- Some clients may need help, and you should be ready to offer this when you see someone in difficulty.

Arrange food on a plate so that it looks tempting

Keys to Good Practice: Serving food and drink

- ✔ Arrange food attractively on the plate.
- ✔ Serve food hot, but avoid serving scalding hot food.
- ✔ When using a tray to carry food to the table reduce the risk of spillage, for example by using non-slip mats.
- ✔ Make sure that salt, pepper and sauces are in suitable containers which are unlikely to spill and are within easy reach of the client.
- ✔ Check out your own personal hygiene – always wash your hands and tie long hair back.
- ✔ Provide napkins or similar protection.
- ✔ Avoid tucking napkins around the client's neck as they may find this demeaning.
- ✔ Be ready to offer assistance when you see that someone is having difficulty.

Violet Walker on her 80th birthday – see page 112

Case study: Violet Walker

Violet Walker has recently had to sell her maisonette to move into a residential care home near her daughter's home. Violet is 82 years old and was diagnosed with **Parkinson's disease** 10 years ago. Before moving to Greyfriars House, Violet looked after herself. A friend took her shopping once a week and she was able to cook and to care for herself generally. Violet enjoys painting, making tapestries and cross-stitch and is a keen reader and Scrabble player. Recently her Parkinson's symptoms have meant that she is unable to do as much craft work as she would like. She has also become very stooped and finds it painful to keep her head up in order to talk to people and to eat at the table. After a few falls it was reluctantly agreed by Violet and her family that she needed more care. When in her own home, Violet usually ate her meals on her lap in her special 'easy-rise' chair and used a straw to take drinks. She still has her own teeth and enjoys most food – including very hot curries! Now that she is in Greyfriars, she has breakfast, afternoon tea and supper in her own room (in her special chair) but joins other residents each lunchtime as she is encouraged to be – and indeed wants to be – sociable.

Questions

1 What are Violet's special needs with regard to eating and drinking?

2 How could you make sure Violet's needs are met?

3 How would you ensure that Violet's preferences are respected?

Helping people with special needs to eat and drink

Eating and drinking involves complex physical and mental coordination. We learn from a young age to recognise food, to use cutlery and how to feed ourselves. These skills quickly become automatic. Later in life we learn to plan for mealtimes, to go shopping and to cook as part of a daily routine. Special needs in this area means that clients need help with some parts of eating and drinking, often for the following reasons:

- They have to follow a special diet, for example a diabetic or gluten-free diet.
- They have difficulties with chewing or swallowing, perhaps because of a stroke or dementia.

- They have physical problems in coordinating the movements necessary to feed themselves, for example with cerebral palsy.
- They have restricted arm and hand movements, for example not being able to hold cutlery, perhaps because of rheumatoid arthritis.
- They may be partially sighted or blind and unable to see what they are eating.
- They may have difficulty chewing because of poorly fitting dentures or sore gums.

Maintaining independence

As eating and drinking is a very personal activity, all clients should be encouraged to do it for themselves. If you have to feed a client, you should be aware that it can be very embarrassing for them and you should do everything you can to make it as pleasant a task as possible. Try other strategies before deciding that feeding a client is necessary, for example specially adapted utensils may be all that is needed – or you may only need to help by cutting up their food.

There is a wide range of gadgets and utensils which can help people with different problems to maintain their independence both when preparing food and when eating and drinking. An occupational therapist will be able to give advice on the appropriate aids.

For visually impaired people

Almost half of visually impaired people are unable to cook for themselves. They find it difficult to access information on healthy eating, and labels on food packaging are almost impossible to read for anyone with impaired vision. They also face many hazards in the kitchen and ideally need a kitchen that is designed to reduce the risk of accidents such as burns, scalds and cuts. There are many gadgets which help to make preparing and eating food much easier and safer. These include:

- a dark chopping board for light-coloured food and a light chopping board for dark-coloured food
- utensils in contrasting colours to the work surface so that they are easier to see

- talking scales and scales with a Braille face
- liquid level indicators – devices which fit over the side of a cup and sound a bleep when the required liquid level is reached.

For people with limited dexterity

Below is a range of kitchen devices to help people with limited hand movements:

- vegetable peelers and scrapers with large grip-handles, a clamp to attach to the work surface and mounted in a slip-resistant base
- saw knives – a handle/handgrip set at an angle to the blade provides an easier cutting action
- stabilisers – clamps and holders to secure jars, and so on, so they can be opened with one hand
- slip-resistant mats to stop bowls and plates sliding around
- boards with spikes and raised edges to hold food in place for cutting and buttering
- lightweight thick-handled angled cutlery – easier to grip and manoeuvre
- tippers – devices to hold a teapot or kettle while it boils and provide support for easier tilting when pouring
- lap trays – rigid trays with a bean bag on the underside that moulds around the user's legs for stability.

For people with dementia

More than 700,000 people in the UK have **dementia**. One-third of people with dementia live on their own, one-third live with a carer, and the remainder live in long-term care. Dementia affects a person's ability to learn, and people with dementia often find it difficult to learn and remember how to use new equipment. Gas and electric hobs are frequently left turned on, empty kettles are switched on, and saucepans are allowed to boil dry. People with dementia may also lose their sense of time, making it difficult for them to follow the normal routines of breakfast, lunch and dinner. Some devices to help them are:

- Cut-off devices and other adaptations can help to reduce risks such as forgetting to turn off gas or electric hobs.

- Microwave ovens – these avoid certain risks but are only useful when the person with dementia has experience of using such equipment, for example the person must know that metal containers should never be used in a microwave oven.
- Specialist eating equipment can help people eat and drink independently for longer.
- Providing 'finger food', which can be eaten while walking around, often helps when the person with dementia does not recognise mealtime routines.
- Picture menus, pictures of meals, will help people to choose their preferred food.

Part of a range of ergonomically designed, dishwasher proof cutlery

A snap-on food barrier to enable food to be pushed against whilst on the plate.

Lap tray

A clear polycarbonate cup with 2 lids, one a feeding spout and one an anti-splash device

Aids to eating

However, there will always be some people who need your assistance with eating and drinking. The Keys to Good Practice on page 116 explain how to help a person while maintaining their dignity and independence.

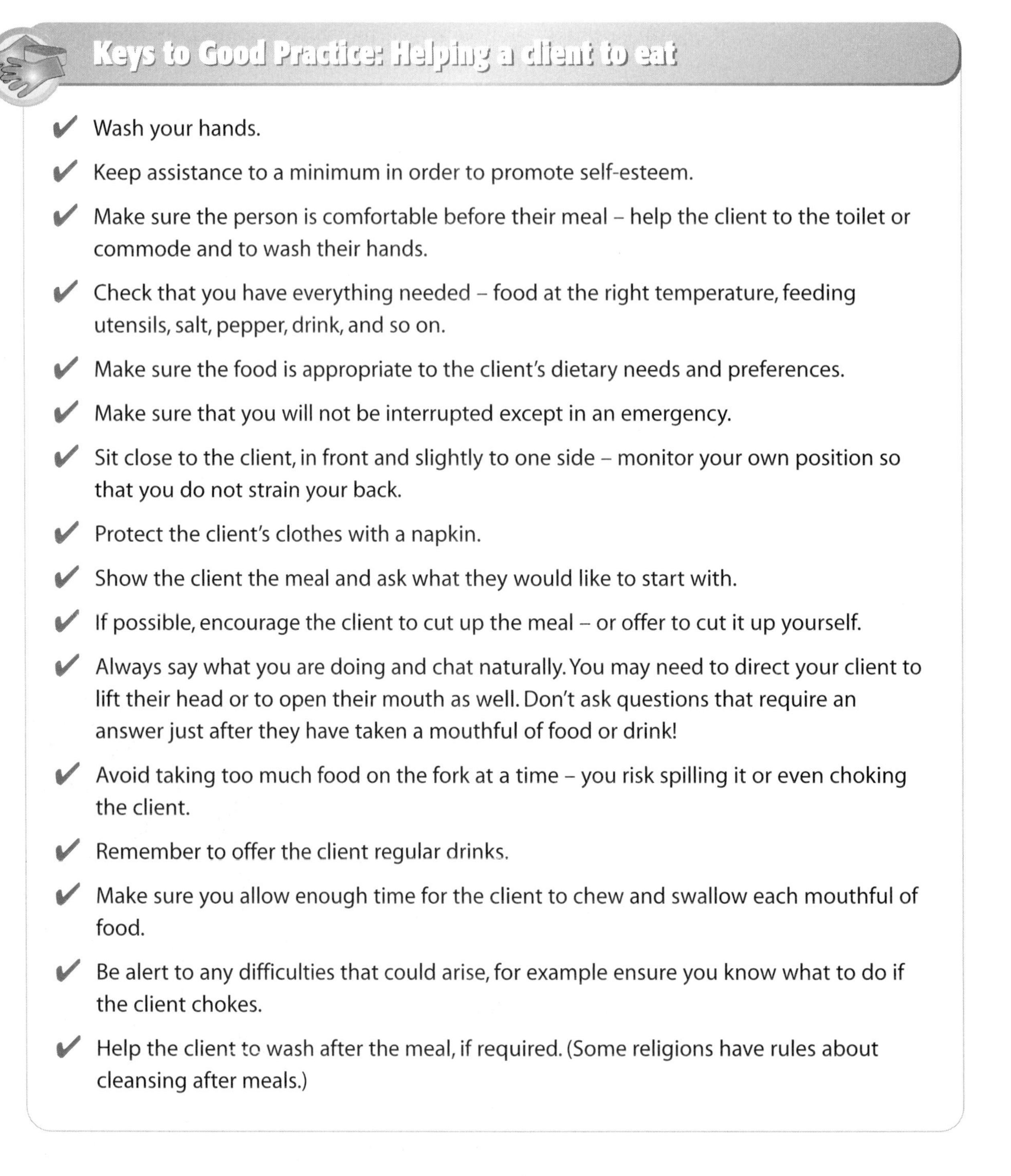

Keys to Good Practice: Helping a client to eat

- ✔ Wash your hands.
- ✔ Keep assistance to a minimum in order to promote self-esteem.
- ✔ Make sure the person is comfortable before their meal – help the client to the toilet or commode and to wash their hands.
- ✔ Check that you have everything needed – food at the right temperature, feeding utensils, salt, pepper, drink, and so on.
- ✔ Make sure the food is appropriate to the client's dietary needs and preferences.
- ✔ Make sure that you will not be interrupted except in an emergency.
- ✔ Sit close to the client, in front and slightly to one side – monitor your own position so that you do not strain your back.
- ✔ Protect the client's clothes with a napkin.
- ✔ Show the client the meal and ask what they would like to start with.
- ✔ If possible, encourage the client to cut up the meal – or offer to cut it up yourself.
- ✔ Always say what you are doing and chat naturally. You may need to direct your client to lift their head or to open their mouth as well. Don't ask questions that require an answer just after they have taken a mouthful of food or drink!
- ✔ Avoid taking too much food on the fork at a time – you risk spilling it or even choking the client.
- ✔ Remember to offer the client regular drinks.
- ✔ Make sure you allow enough time for the client to chew and swallow each mouthful of food.
- ✔ Be alert to any difficulties that could arise, for example ensure you know what to do if the client chokes.
- ✔ Help the client to wash after the meal, if required. (Some religions have rules about cleansing after meals.)

A coordinated approach to providing food in hospital

When a survey revealed that many patients were leaving hospital undernourished, Tembridge Hospital decided it was time to act. Patients and relatives were complaining of poor quality food and of food being left at the ends of beds. Busy nurses did not have the time to assist patients who needed help with eating. The hospital called in a nutrition specialist and, as a result, completely changed the way it produced and served food to patients. It developed a coordinated approach which included the following:

- Full-time ward hostesses were introduced on certain wards, including the two wards for elderly people. The hostesses serve food and help those people who can't eat by themselves.
- Occupational therapists visited and ensured that specialised eating equipment was made available to enable people to eat independently.
- The menus were reviewed. They now offer more choice for patients, ensuring that the food reflects the cultural diversity of the patients.

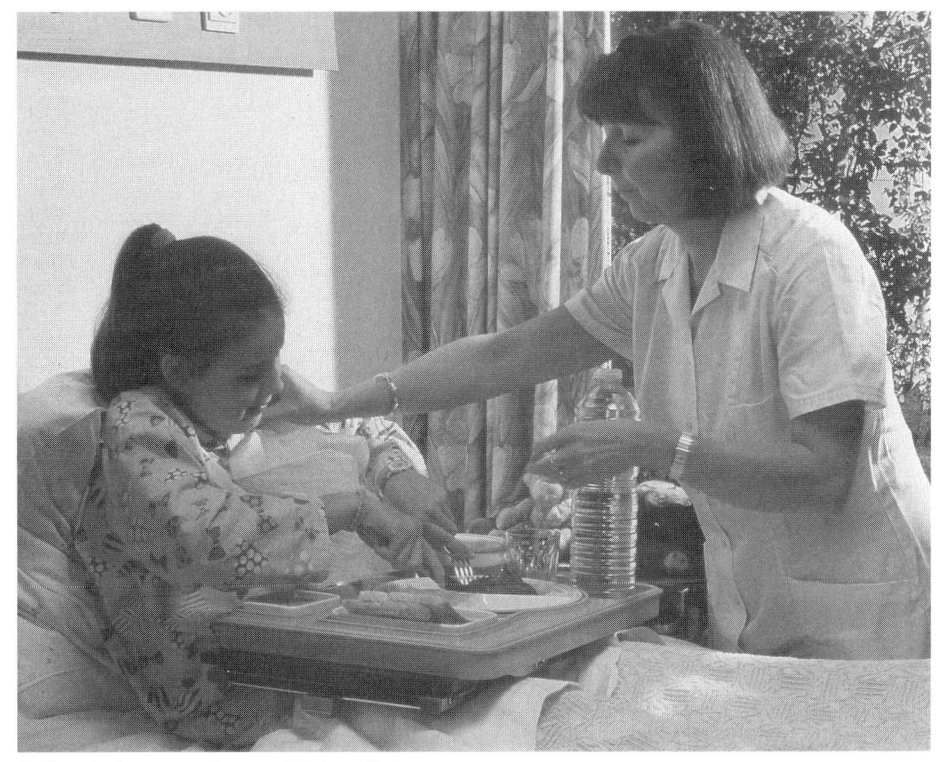

Patient being served a meal in hospital

Difficulties with chewing and swallowing

Most of us do not have to think about the need to chew before we swallow. Swallowing comes easily to many people – we swallow at least 500 times a day. Swallowing involves voluntary and automatic actions which can easily be impaired by the physical effects of certain medical conditions, for example **stroke (CVA)** and dementia. People who have difficulties in swallowing may hold food in the side of their mouths and then spit it out when they are alone. Speech/language therapists have the most expertise in the management of swallowing problems. It is important that you are aware of and sensitive to the possibility that your client may experience difficulties with swallowing.

Helping clients with shopping and cooking

Following the closure of large institutions for people with learning disabilities and those with mental illness, many people are now being cared for in the community. They may live alone in a flat or with other clients in 'cluster' housing. In either case, each client will be allocated a key worker who will plan the package of care. You may be involved in this kind of care work. Your client may need help with shopping and cooking. Depending on the person's needs, the care worker could:

- accompany the client while shopping
- check the dates on packaged food in the client's house
- help to store food correctly
- supervise cooking.

Case study: Food hygiene dilemmas

Sharma Seth

It is 6 pm and one of Sharma Seth's jobs as care assistant in Westbury Hospital is to collect meals from the ward kitchen to take to the patients. She reaches the kitchen only a couple of minutes after the caterers have left. The food is ready but Sharma notices immediately that a cat – often seen straying around the hospital grounds – is washing itself in the corner of the kitchen. She chases it out but she also notices that it has left paw prints on the work surfaces next to the food trolley.

Michael Townsend

A week ago Jack Tribiani had a stroke which left him with a weakness down one side of his body. He now finds it difficult to feed himself and needs assistance. At 12.30 pm nursing assistant Michael Townsend arrives in Mr Tribiani's room to help him with his lunch. As Michael turns from feeding the patient to prepare the next mouthful, he sees that a bluebottle fly has settled on the portion of meat on the plate.

Lisa Riley

It is a hectic day at Green Rushes Nursery and Lisa Riley has been rushed off her feet all morning. On the rota she sees that it is her turn to bring the children's lunch from the kitchen. Having been so busy, Lisa has left it later than she would normally. As she leaves the kitchen and makes her way down the corridor back to the nursery, several forks and serving spoons fall from the tray she is carrying to the floor. Lisa puts down the tray on the floor to pick up the cutlery. She knows that the floor is clean as it is thoroughly washed every morning before the children arrive.

Narinda Adams

Narinda Adams is a volunteer care assistant at Whiteleys Day Centre. One of her jobs is to serve the lunches. On going to the kitchen she finds that the dishwasher is out of order. Most of the washing up has already been done, but Narinda needs plates for 16 people and there are only 12 clean ones. She sets about washing them herself, using the cloth that has been left on the draining board. She also dries the plates thoroughly with the only tea towel available, although it is quite damp and has a musty smell. Having done this, Narinda serves the food to the clients.

Questions

For each of the four scenarios above, decide:

1. what is the particular problem regarding food hygiene
2. what the care worker *should* do or *should* have done
3. the reasons for your decision.

Special occasions

You may be asked to help prepare food for a trip out – a picnic or a barbecue, for example. The range of foods chosen for these occasions will almost always contain **high risk foods**, so extra care must be taken when preparing them.

Making sandwiches

Making sandwiches and filled rolls usually involves a lot of handling, so personal hygiene is very important. Sandwiches are often filled with high risk foods and should be handled and stored like any other high risk food. You should make sandwiches as close to the time of eating as possible so that they are fresh. If this is not practical, make the sandwiches and put them in the fridge. Here are some tips to help you prepare 'safe' sandwiches:

- Try to avoid handling food unnecessarily by using tongs and other utensils.
- Wear gloves, if you prefer, but remember that they should be used for one task only, for example, breaking up a cooked chicken for sandwiches. When you start the next task, wear new gloves – and remember to wash your hands too.
- Never use the same utensils for raw meats and ready-to-eat foods such as cooked meats, unless they have been thoroughly cleaned, sanitised and dried.
- Cooked food and other food that is ready to eat, such as salads, should always be placed on clean and dry serving dishes.

Safety tip!

As making sandwiches involves lots of handling, never make sandwiches when you are ill.

Barbecues and picnics

Summer is a time for picnics and barbecues, but eating (and cooking) outdoors in hot weather can bring many problems for food safety.

What are the problems?

- In summer time, foods can quickly reach the **temperature danger zone** (8°C–63°C) and food poisoning bacteria multiply rapidly in the heat.
- Raw meats such as burgers, sausages and chicken can carry food poisoning bacteria.
- If raw meats are not cooked properly, or if they come into contact with food, or surfaces and equipment used to prepare ready-to-eat food, there is a serious risk of illness.
- Barbecues vary a great deal in how well they cook the food. Some barbecues are too hot in parts and not hot enough in others. A brown or charred appearance does not mean meat is cooked right through. Thicker meat products such as 'quarter pounder' beef-burgers may look cooked on the outside before they are cooked throughout.

When preparing for an outdoor meal – either a barbecue or a picnic – you need to be extra careful about food poisoning risks. The principles remain the same as for any food handling.

Keys to Good Practice: Safe barbecues

Preparation:

- ✔ Always wash your hands thoroughly – before preparing food, after touching raw meat and before eating.
- ✔ Make sure all work surfaces, cooking and eating utensils are spotlessly clean before use.
- ✔ Cover all food whether in the fridge or on the work surface.
- ✔ Keep pets away from food, dishes and preparation surfaces.
- ✔ Light the barbecue well in advance, making sure you use enough charcoal and that the coals are very hot – wait until the coals glow red (with a powdery grey surface) before starting to cook.
- ✔ Ensure raw meat is completely defrosted in the fridge or a microwave before barbecuing so that it cooks more evenly, unless the cooking instructions state otherwise.
- ✔ Always use clean cloths for wiping surfaces, utensils and hands. Never use a cloth to dry hands or utensils that has also been in contact with raw meat. Use separate cloths for each task, preferably disposable paper towels.

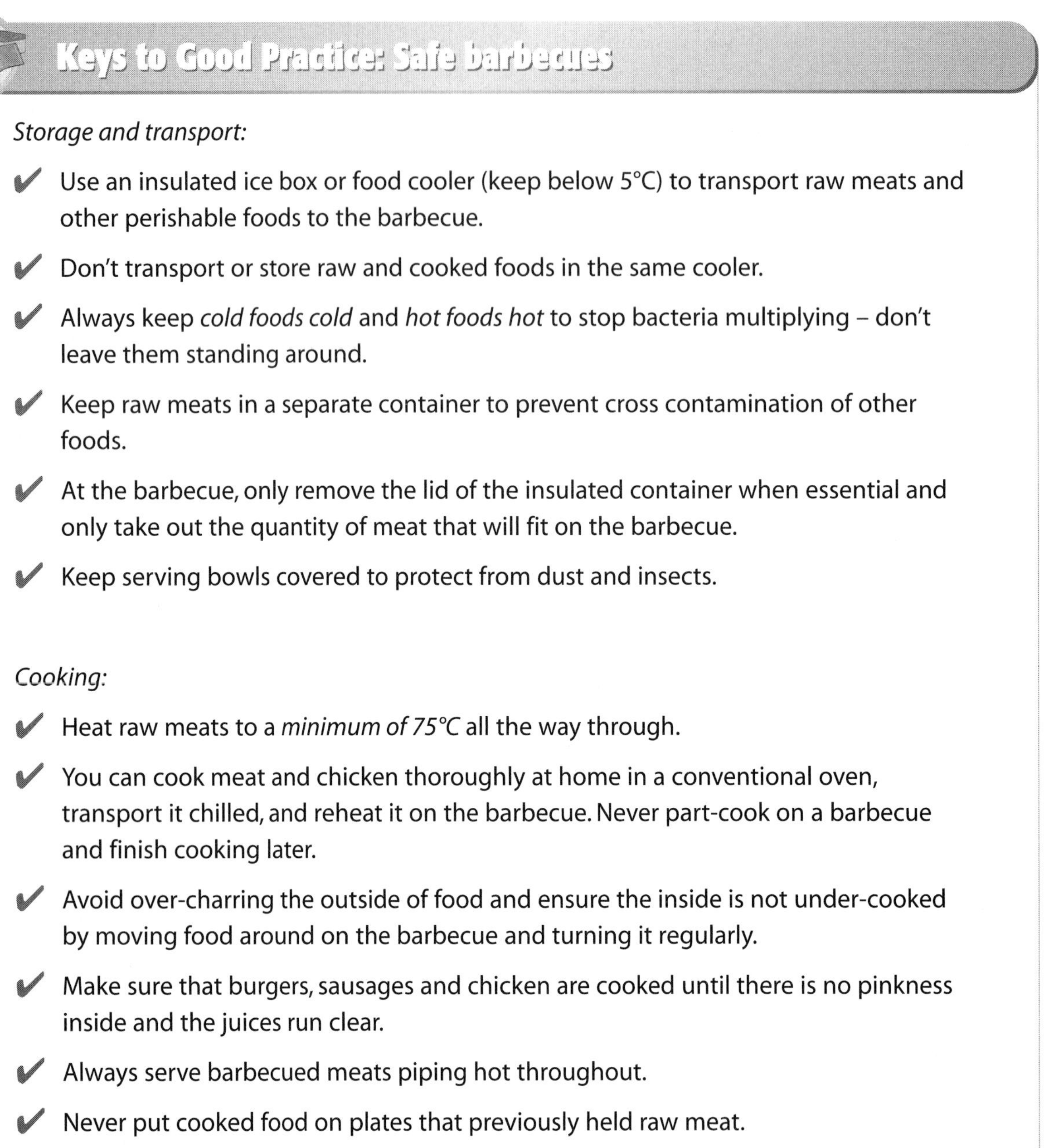

Keys to Good Practice: Safe barbecues

Storage and transport:

- ✔ Use an insulated ice box or food cooler (keep below 5°C) to transport raw meats and other perishable foods to the barbecue.
- ✔ Don't transport or store raw and cooked foods in the same cooler.
- ✔ Always keep *cold foods cold* and *hot foods hot* to stop bacteria multiplying – don't leave them standing around.
- ✔ Keep raw meats in a separate container to prevent cross contamination of other foods.
- ✔ At the barbecue, only remove the lid of the insulated container when essential and only take out the quantity of meat that will fit on the barbecue.
- ✔ Keep serving bowls covered to protect from dust and insects.

Cooking:

- ✔ Heat raw meats to a *minimum of 75°C* all the way through.
- ✔ You can cook meat and chicken thoroughly at home in a conventional oven, transport it chilled, and reheat it on the barbecue. Never part-cook on a barbecue and finish cooking later.
- ✔ Avoid over-charring the outside of food and ensure the inside is not under-cooked by moving food around on the barbecue and turning it regularly.
- ✔ Make sure that burgers, sausages and chicken are cooked until there is no pinkness inside and the juices run clear.
- ✔ Always serve barbecued meats piping hot throughout.
- ✔ Never put cooked food on plates that previously held raw meat.
- ✔ Throw away any barbecued food left out for more than two hours in very hot weather.

The same care needs to be taken when preparing and serving picnic food:

Keys to Good Practice: Picnics

- ✔ Prepare what you can at home so that you don't have to handle food unnecessarily on the picnic, particularly where there are no hand washing facilities.
- ✔ Bring moist cleansing wipes to clean hands if there is no water at the picnic site.
- ✔ Don't pack food for a picnic if it has just been cooked or is still warm.
- ✔ Keep perishable foods cool – below 5°C. Use an insulated cool box.
- ✔ Store the cool box in the coolest part of the car (not the boot) and keep it out of the sun.
- ✔ Eat the picnic within a few hours of leaving home.
- ✔ Cover food when it is not being eaten to avoid contamination by insects.
- ✔ Take perishable leftovers home in a cool box – check it still has ice. If leftovers are allowed to remain in the temperature danger zone (8°C–63°C) they could cause food poisoning. If in doubt, throw leftover food out.

Case study: Eating away from home

Food poisoning is more likely when people are catering for large groups, research suggests. Experts from the Public Health Laboratory Service (PHLS) say that social events such as barbecues and Christmas dinners are the kind of situations in which cooks do not stick to food hygiene rules. Problems can be as simple as a lack of space to keep all prepared food in the fridge.

Researchers found that although the trend for such infections was going down, 88 per cent of cases classed as outbreaks (affecting more than one household) were linked to social gatherings. Reasons given for this were that people may be in a hurry and less likely to remember their basic food safety knowledge, for example they might not wash their hands in-between preparing raw and cooked food. Also, the quantities being prepared might mean it was not possible to store the food in the ideal way.

Question

Prepare a leaflet on how to provide safe, hygienic food for a cold buffet party. The leaflet should include information on:

❑ preparation ❑ storage ❑ transport ❑ cooking ❑ serving.

Chapter 9

Cleaning and disinfecting food areas

Protecting yourself and others from the risks of food poisoning involves more than handling and storing food safely and hygienically. You will also need to make sure that the food preparation area is clean and tidy. Surprisingly, this may not be enough – even the cleanest, tidiest kitchen is home to millions of food poisoning bacteria! Usually bacteria can be safely controlled by heating (cooking) or by cooling (refrigeration), but they can easily spread from our hands to tea-towels, to utensils and work surfaces, and end up contaminating food. To prevent this you will need to take extra steps to make sure that work surfaces, utensils, equipment, and so on, are thoroughly cleansed and disinfected where appropriate.

This chapter looks at how to clean and disinfect food areas, utensils and equipment so that they are safe to use. It covers the following topics:

- ❑ **Good housekeeping.**
- ❑ **Cleaning.**
- ❑ **Disinfection.**
- ❑ **Methods of cleaning and disinfection.**
- ❑ **Care and storage of cleaning equipment.**
- ❑ **Waste disposal.**
- ❑ **Refuse areas.**

Good housekeeping

Good housekeeping will help you to make sure that the food you prepare is safe, clean and wholesome. It involves:

- ➤ keeping the workplace clean and tidy
- ➤ using safe working practices.

The smooth running of any care establishment largely depends on its housekeeping policy.

A successful policy will benefit both staff and clients:

- High morale – staff are likely to take more pride in their work and to pay closer attention to their personal hygiene.
- Better working conditions – a clean, tidy workplace is a more pleasant environment to work in.
- Safety – foods which are prepared with clean equipment and in spotless surroundings are hygienically safer.
- Fewer accidents – people working in clean, tidy surroundings are less likely to have accidents or be exposed to environmental health hazards.
- Efficiency – a well-organised and well-run workplace encourages efficiency.
- Less waste – properly designed and well-maintained equipment operated with effective techniques creates less waste, so the need for cleaning and waste disposal is reduced.

Cleaning

Cleaning helps to get rid of harmful bacteria that can contaminate food, utensils, equipment and food preparation and storage areas. Along with temperature controls, cleaning is very important in protecting food from contamination.

Cleaning is the process of making something free from dirt and contamination. Depending on what you are cleaning, this may involve:

- wiping
- scrubbing
- scouring
- sweeping
- brushing
- rubbing.

Cleaning may also use heat (hot water) and/or chemicals (such as **detergents**). It can include the disinfection of equipment and work surfaces (see pages 132–3).

Cleaning helps to get rid of harmful bacteria

The aims of cleaning

- *To remove food debris, so reducing the risk of bacterial growth and food poisoning.*
- *To protect food from bacterial contamination.*
- *To avoid attracting* ***food pests*** *such as insects, rodents, and so on.*
- *To maintain a safe environment, for example to prevent accidents caused by a greasy floor.*
- *To ensure a pleasant and safe working environment.*
- *To promote a good image to staff and clients.*

Using detergents

Cleaning involves using detergents, such as washing-up liquid and special de-greasers, and these (with the use of hot water) will be able to destroy some bacteria. Certain washing-up liquids claim to be 'antibacterial' but are effective only if used neat (undiluted) on cloths and sponges. Once diluted, they will not provide the level of disinfection required for certain food equipment and utensils. There will always be some items in the kitchen which you will need to disinfect after they have been washed to prevent food poisoning bacteria multiplying.

Disinfection

Disinfection helps to reduce bacteria to a low, safe level. You can disinfect items using either:

- special chemicals intended for food use
- hot water at around 82°C
- steam.

Keys to Good Practice: Using chemicals safely and effectively

- ✔ Always store chemicals in their own labelled containers away from food.
- ✔ Always read the manufacturers' instructions carefully and follow them.
- ✔ Always make sure that everyone using the chemicals knows how to use them correctly.
- ✔ Wear protective clothing such as rubber gloves and aprons.
- ✔ Never make up solutions of chemicals a long time in advance. Many chemicals are unstable once they have been diluted and will rapidly become less effective.
- ✔ Never mix chemicals or solutions of chemicals. Chemicals may react with each other if mixed causing them to lose their effectiveness or to release harmful gases.
- ✔ Never use chemicals in concentrations greater than those recommended by the manufacturer – increasing the concentration will not necessarily increase the effectiveness of the chemical and can be dangerous.

Heat and chemical disinfection are often used in combination and should always be done *after* cleaning. This is because most disinfectants are not designed to remove dirt and grease. Their effectiveness relies on any dirt being removed first. The exception to this are **sanitising** agents, which clean and disinfect at the same time.

Methods of cleaning and disinfection

'Clean as you go' cleaning

The best way to keep a kitchen clean is by cleaning as you go:

- You should clear and clean up *immediately after* each task, for example you will need to clean and disinfect work surfaces after handling raw meat or poultry.
- If you spill some food, clear it up straight away and then clean the surface thoroughly.
- Regularly clean and disinfect items and areas where there are likely to be food poisoning bacteria during the work period – this includes work surfaces and chopping boards.

The cleaning schedule

A cleaning schedule is a timetable used in all food premises that sets out when and how different items and areas should be cleaned and who should actually do the cleaning. It is a good way to make sure that surfaces and equipment are cleaned when they need to be. When drawing up a cleaning schedule you will need to work out what needs cleaning every day, or more than once a day, and what needs cleaning less frequently. Your schedule should show:

- *what* needs to be cleaned – utensil, work surface or floor
- *who* is responsible for doing the cleaning – which staff member
- *when* (how often it needs to be done) – after each use, daily, weekly, and so on
- *how* the cleaning should be done
- *the person* responsible for monitoring that the cleaning has been carried out effectively.

A separate chart could provide more detailed cleaning instructions for staff showing:

- what cleaning chemicals should be used for each specific task
- how the chemicals should be used, including how much they should be diluted and how long they should be left on the surface, as recommended by the manufacturer
- how the chemicals should be stored
- where the chemicals should be stored (in a separate area away from food).

A sample cleaning schedule

Item to be cleaned	Product to be used	How to use	Protective clothing to be worn	How often?	To be cleaned by
Floors	Heavy duty detergent	Prepare a hot solution (half a cupful per bucket of water). Use a clean mop. Allow a few minutes for the solution to act. Then mop again with fresh clean water.	Rubber gloves, suitable footwear	Daily	Emma
Deep fat fryers	Heavy duty degreaser	Drain off fat when cold. Fill with water, then add degreaser (1 cup per bucket of water). Boil for up to 20 minutes. Brush surrounds with solution. Empty. Then rinse with clean fresh water. Allow to air dry.	Rubber gloves, plastic apron	Every 7 days	Gary
Slicers, mixers, mincers, peelers	Cleansing and sanitising powder	Prepare a hot solution (half cupful per bucket of water). Place moveable parts in solution and soak for 2 minutes. Brush or sponge all parts. Rinse with clean fresh water. Allow to air dry.	Rubber gloves, plastic apron	After each use	Ushma
Food preparation surfaces, chopping boards	Cleansing and sanitising powder	Fill shaker with powder, sprinkle onto a moistened surface and scrub. Leave for a few moments for the powder to act. Wipe the surface with a clean moist cloth and allow to air dry.	Rubber gloves, plastic apron	After each use	Holly

Source: East Herts Council website

How to clean and disinfect

Regular and thorough cleaning is needed to prevent the contamination of food, for example if you are cleaning a fridge or freezer, remember to make sure that the food is kept at a safe temperature below the temperature danger zone.

Quick fact

The temperature danger zone is 8°C–63°C. This is the temperature range in which food poisoning bacteria may grow.

You will need to follow the six stages shown below each time you carry out a wet cleaning and disinfection task.

Keys to Good Practice: Wet cleaning and disinfecting: the six stages

1 Pre-clean. Remove any obvious loose food and dirt, for example scrape chopping boards and plates and soak pans.

2 Main clean. Use hot soapy water (diluted detergent) to remove grease and any remaining food and dirt.

3 Rinse. Use hot, clean water to remove traces of detergent and food.

4 Disinfection. Use a chemical disinfectant to kill bacteria – make sure it is left on for the correct contact time.

5 Final rinse. Rinse with hot, clean water to remove disinfectant (if rinsing is included in the instructions on the label).

6 Dry. Allow to dry naturally, if possible, or dry with a disposable paper cloth. If you have to use a fabric cloth, it must be clean and dry and used for one batch of drying only.

Note: Sanitising agents are sometimes used to reduce the number of cleaning stages (combining steps 2 to 4).

Equipment hygiene: work surfaces and utensils

Cleaning work surfaces

Work surfaces need to be cleaned and disinfected regularly, as described below. This should be done on a 'clean as you go' basis and should be allocated to a staff member on the cleaning schedule.

1 Protect food from contamination. Cover and put in the fridge if possible.
2 Remove any loose pieces of food and dirt.
3 Wash surface with hot water and an appropriate cleanser or detergent, using a cloth or scourer.
4 Rinse with hot water and a clean cloth.
5 Apply a chemical disinfectant, following the instruction about contact time.
6 Rinse with clean water.
7 Leave to air dry or use a disposable paper towel.

Cleaning utensils in a dishwasher

Using a dishwasher is an effective way to make sure that dishes, glasses and utensils are really clean. This is because dishwashers use very hot water (rinsing at 82°C or hotter) which kills bacteria. You should always remove any obvious food and dirt before putting things in the dishwasher. Make sure that your dishwasher is working effectively and using water that is hot enough. A good way to clean and disinfect most chopping boards is to put them in the dishwasher (but check first that they are dishwasher safe).

Cleaning utensils by hand

Ideally, you should use two sinks side by side when washing-up by hand. If only one sink is available, make sure that all items are rinsed thoroughly using clean hot water after initial washing.

Keys to Good Practice: Washing-up by hand

1. Wear rubber gloves to protect hands from hot water and chemicals.
2. Wash the least dirty things, such as glasses, first.
3. Scrape and rinse off any obvious food and dirt.
4. Wash the items (in the first sink if you have one) with hot water (55°C) and washing-up liquid, using a cloth or brush. Replace the water if it becomes greasy or too cool.
5. Rinse in very hot water (82°C) leaving items to soak for 30 seconds (in the second sink if you have one). If possible, use a mesh draining basket to lift items out of the water.
6. Leave to air dry if possible. Alternatively, use a clean tea-towel and change tea-towels frequently (at least once a day).

It is important to make sure that you put away plates and bowls only when they are completely dry. Pools of water can collect in washed dishes providing a warm, damp place for bacteria to grow. Single-use disposable cloths placed between or underneath kitchen utensils, crockery and cutlery will absorb water, preventing the risk of contamination.

Disinfecting utensils

You can use a dishwasher to disinfect chemicals if it has a hot wash and drying cycle. Use the hottest temperature setting (usually 65°C).

If a dishwasher is not available, you will need to disinfect in a sink using a chemical disinfectant or very hot water. Always wear protective clothing – gloves and apron – to do this.

- If using a chemical disinfectant such as a sodium hypochlorite (bleach) solution, ensure that it can be safely used to disinfect utensils used for eating, drinking and cooking. Follow the instructions on the container carefully, as different disinfectants work in different ways.
- If you are using very hot water, take extra care to avoid being scalded. All utensils must then be dried thoroughly before they are re-used. Air drying is best but tea-towels can be used if they are clean.

What should you disinfect? Often bacteria can collect in places that you might not expect. Anything that is touched by food or by people's hands could be covered in bacteria. You will therefore need to disinfect the items shown in the table below.

What to disinfect?

Hand contact surfaces	Food contact surfaces	Bacterial 'hotspots'
Fridge/freezer handles	Work surfaces, chopping boards, preparation areas	Cloths, brushes and mops
Tap handles, cupboard and drawer handles	Slicers, mixers and food processors	Waste bins and their lids
Telephones and light switches	Knives, tongs, can openers and other utensils	Telephone receivers, toilet door handles

Care and storage of cleaning equipment

To prevent bacterial **cross contamination**, it is recommended that:

- All cloths, mops, buckets, brushes and so on, should be used for specific purposes. Colour codes can be used to identify those used for cleaning utensils, work surfaces and the floor.
- Cleaning cloths should be disposable (thrown away daily) if woven fabric cloths are used. However, they could be changed once a day and laundered.
- Mops and cloths should be cleaned and disinfected soon after use and left to dry in the air. Do not leave mops and cloths to soak in disinfectant for longer than the manufacturer's recommended time as this may enable bacteria to become resistant to the chemicals.
- All chemicals and cleaning equipment must be stored in a locked cupboard out of reach of children and away from food.

Quick facts

- ✔ The average dishcloth can contain 100 million bacteria after just one week's use.
- ✔ 79 per cent of people change their dishcloths less than once a month.
- ✔ 51 per cent of households do not use separate chopping boards for raw and cooked foods.
- ✔ Hot-air hand dryers actually increase bacteria levels by up to 500 per cent.
- ✔ The rubbing or abrasive action of a paper towel removes bacteria from hands after washing.

Choosing cleaning products

All cleansers, detergents and disinfectants should be clearly labelled and recommended for use with food. You will need different products to do different tasks:

- Detergents help to break down grease and remove dirt when used with hot water. Most bacteria will survive cleaning by detergents.
- Disinfectants are chemicals that reduce pathogenic (dangerous) bacteria to a safe level, but they are unable to kill all food poisoning bacteria and their spores. They should be used *after* cleaning.
- Sanitisers combine a detergent and a disinfectant so will both clean and disinfect – providing there is enough contact time (follow the manufacturers' instructions).

You are likely to need the following products:

- a degreaser or 'deep' cleaner for high-fat situations, for example a greasy pan or deep-fat fryer bowl
- a standard detergent for washing-up
- a suitable sanitiser to disinfect surfaces, cutting boards and equipment. When used in food preparation areas sanitisers must be of a 'food safe' variety.

Detergents and sanitising products

Further professional advice and guidance can be obtained from one of the specialist companies supplying cleansing agents to the food industry (listed in Yellow Pages under Janitorial Supplies).

Use of cleaning cloths

Cloths used to clean dishes and surfaces as well as tea-towels can also spread bacteria. Make sure you wash and dry them thoroughly and replace them regularly – at least once a day. Throw away worn or damaged cloths and tea-towels.

Safety tip!

Use paper towels or disposable cloths wherever possible.

Scientific tests have shown that fabric cleaning cloths are the most common cause of **cross contamination** in the kitchen. This is because bacteria can multiply quickly in moist conditions. These bacteria may then be transferred from one surface to another, particularly after use on raw food preparation surfaces.

If paper towels or disposable single-use towels are not available, then cleaning cloths should be:

- designated for certain areas in the kitchen – they can be colour coded so as to identify their use
- kept clean and disinfected at least daily
- used once and then put into a bucket containing a sanitiser and disinfected between uses.

To disinfect a cleaning cloth, soak the cloth in a properly diluted solution of bleach or Milton® between tasks. This solution must be changed at least every 12 hours.

Checking for cracks and damage

All equipment should be checked regularly for signs of damage. Cracks, chips and scratches provide a home to bacteria. Chipped or cracked crockery should never be used. Report any damaged crockery or equipment to your supervisor, who will decide on the appropriate course of action.

Waste disposal

As food waste can quickly rot, it can become a source of food for insects and rodents and thus a source of disease. Its smell can also be a problem as it pollutes the environment and may attract rodents and other animals; and used packaging material may provide a comfortable nest for rodents and other vermin. Dealing with kitchen waste is an important part of keeping food preparation areas clean.

Indoor waste bins should have a well-fitting lid and preferably be foot-operated.

Keys to Good Practice: Indoor waste disposal

- ✔ Line waste bins with a disposable polythene bag.
- ✔ Place the waste bin within easy reach of food handlers but well away from food sources such as cupboards and fridges.
- ✔ Clear away waste from food preparation areas as soon as possible – waste should be collected regularly from the premises.
- ✔ Clean waste bins after emptying – using plastic bin liners makes cleaning easier.
- ✔ Regularly check waste bins are in good condition – cracked bins can harbour bacteria.
- ✔ For dry refuse use paper sacks held in a frame with a close fitting lid.
- ✔ Empty indoor waste bins as soon as they become full and place in outside bins.
- ✔ Always empty and clean waste bins and their lids at the end of the work period.
- ✔ Always wash your hands after handling refuse.

Refuse areas

In food premises it is recommended that a separate fly-proof refuse room should be used to store containers before disposal and that meat and fish waste must be refrigerated.

Rubbish bins are usually stored outside in a separate area which should be paved and drained to make cleaning easier.

All waste should be bagged before putting in the outside bins and you should check that the lids fit securely – to prevent foxes, cats, dogs and birds from gaining access. If the bins regularly become overfull, inform your supervisor or manager who may need to arrange extra bins or additional refuse collections.

Knowledge Test

Choose the right answer in each case.

1 Which is the *most* risky way to wash dishes?

- **a** In a dishwasher.
- **b** Soak them in warm water and soap for a few hours, then in the same water wash them with a sponge.
- **c** Wash them soon after eating and allow to air dry.

2 Which of the following products should be used to help reduce the presence of food poisoning bacteria on kitchen work surfaces?

- **a** Detergent
- **b** Disinfectant
- **c** Sanitiser

3 What is cleaning?

- **a** Making sure that surfaces and equipment look clean.
- **b** Brushing and wiping surfaces until they are free from smears and streaks.
- **c** Removing soil, dirt and grease in order to keep workplaces safe.

4 What is meant by 'clean as you go'?

- **a** Making sure that everything is clean before you leave for the day.
- **b** Carrying out cleaning procedures as you work.
- **c** Making sure that you always present a clean and tidy appearance.

(Answers on page 181.)

Chapter 10

Control of pests in the workplace

Food pests such as insects, rodents and birds pose a serious risk to health if they are allowed to come into contact with food. They are carriers of pathogenic bacteria which if transferred to food can cause food poisoning. You will need to be particularly alert to pests and know how to deal with them.

This chapter will help you to recognise the different types of food pest, the way they spread disease, what to do to stop them entering the food area and how to deal with infestations. Topics covered include:

- ❑ What are food pests?
- ❑ How to recognise and deal with food pests.
- ❑ Complying with the law.

What are food pests?

A food pest is any creature which lives in or on human food, causing damage or contamination, or both. The main types of pest are:

- ➤ insects – flies and cockroaches
- ➤ insects in stored products – for example beetles, mites and weevils
- ➤ rodents – rats and mice
- ➤ wild birds – starlings, pigeons, sparrows and magpies.

Insects, rodents and birds

Food pests are attracted to places where food is stored, prepared, sold, served or thrown away. They also like warmth and shelter from cold, wind and rain. They can enter through open windows and doors, or through tiny cracks in walls and around pipes and gratings.

How to recognise and deal with food pests

Insects

Flies

The main flies to look out for are the common housefly, bluebottle and greenbottle.

The common housefly:

- is black and about 8 mm long – its body is covered with fine hairs and bristles which readily pick up dirt particles
- lays up to 1000 eggs in just two weeks – these hatch within 24 hours into maggots and the adult fly appears about a week later
- rarely lives for more than a week.

The common housefly on a piece of raw meat

Bluebottles and greenbottles:

- are larger than houseflies and have shiny, metallic coloured bodies
- make a loud droning buzz
- prefer to lay their eggs on exposed meat
- have a life cycle of 9–21 days between egg and adult.

Bottle fly laying eggs on exposed meat

How flies spread disease

Flies carry pathogenic bacteria and contaminate foods by:

- landing on food and food surfaces and transferring bacteria from their legs and body
- continually defecating (passing faeces) on the food
- regurgitating partly-digested food from a previous meal (which may have been in a dustbin or on animal faeces) on to the food on which they are currently feeding
- depositing their eggs on food
- their dead bodies may end up in food.

Flies have also been shown to carry salmonella and other organisms which cause typhoid fever, dysentery, tuberculosis and **parasitic** worms.

Preventing flies from entering the food area

The best way of preventing flies from entering the food area is to practise good housekeeping. This may involve:

- fitting screens on windows and doors
- installing UV light traps.

Chemical insecticides may be used to kill larvae (pre-adult stage) and adult insects, but you should obtain specialist advice before doing this because of the risks of food contamination.

Cockroaches

The most common species of cockroaches in the UK are the German and Oriental cockroaches. Cockroaches:

- are large (about 24 mm long) and reddish-brown or light-brown insects with whip-like antennae and two pairs of wings
- live about 4–14 months as adults, during which time females can produce up to 50 egg cases – each egg sac contains 12–30 eggs and a female German cockroach would produce about 150 live offspring in an average 8-month lifetime
- can walk, run, jump and sometimes fly
- like to avoid daylight and hide in cracks and crevices
- eat almost anything, including cardboard, and come out to search for food at dusk and early evening
- live at temperatures of 20°C–35°C
- need water
- stay together in groups
- are mostly found in kitchens and toilets, for example behind cookers or in laundry baskets, at the backs of drawers, behind peeling wallpaper.

Cockroaches can be a particular problem in hospitals where they can easily move along water pipes and air ducts.

A cockroach

How cockroaches spread disease

Cockroaches carry pathogenic bacteria and contaminate foods by:

- spreading pathogenic bacteria, salmonella and staphylococcus aureus – they have been associated with outbreaks of gastro-enteritis, typhus and skin diseases
- depositing faecal pellets, moult debris and dead bodies on food.

Contact with cockroaches can lead to a number of allergic illnesses, including dermatitis, urticaria (a skin disease), rhinitis, bronchitis and asthma.

Preventing cockroaches from entering the premises

Good hygiene is essential to prevent or limit infestation. It is vital to stop cockroaches getting food, water and shelter. Here are some ways to help you do this:

- Inspect all boxes, cartons and sacks brought into the kitchen.
- Clean up all spillages immediately.
- Avoid leaving scraps of food on unwashed dishes.
- Keep food in tightly sealed containers.
- Rubbish should be kept in containers with tight lids and rubbish bags should be properly sealed when moved outside.

- Buildings should be regularly inspected, both internally and externally, and repairs to any possible entry routes carried out, for example openings around pipes should be sealed.

Dealing with a cockroach infestation

In the event of a cockroach infestation specialist pest control contractors should be contacted. They will put down insecticides. They usually inspect the premises at night by torchlight to find out the extent of the infestation and which species is involved. Cockroaches are difficult to get rid of and populations usually develop from lone survivors.

Insects in stored foods

There are many species of stored-food pests. Most of these insects are introduced into our homes through infested food, although some enter through cracks, open doors and windows, and so on.

Stored-food pests include:

- flour moths and their larvae
- beetles
- weevils
- psocids (book lice)
- mites.

All items of stored food are at risk. These pests like to feed on flour, cereals, dried food, chocolate, dried fruit and nuts. They do not necessarily carry pathogens and so are not causes of food poisoning. However, they are a nuisance as they make food unwholesome to eat.

Stored-food pest – rice weevils

Preventing stored-food pests from entering the food area

Once again, good housekeeping is essential:

- Keep cupboards clean and free from spillages. Pay close attention to corners, cracks and crevices that can harbour insects.
- In the case of psocids, control humidity (moisture) levels by providing ventilation and dry conditions.
- Keep all containers tightly closed. Put items at risk in tight containers, screw-top jars or other sealable containers.
- Do not overstock shelves with products which will not be used frequently or within a short period of time.
- Buy spices in bottles instead of paper containers.

Dealing with an infestation of stored-food pests

- All foods at risk should be inspected thoroughly, and all infested items thrown away.
- Clean and dry the storage area well.
- Suitable insecticides may be used to kill insects – when using these, take care not to contaminate food.

Rodents

Mice

The house mouse lives alongside humans in many buildings.

- It is an excellent climber and is most active at night.
- It can squeeze through tiny openings (about ½ cm) because its ribs are not joined to a breastbone.
- It breeds rapidly – in ideal conditions one pair of mice can produce up to 2000 young within a year.
- It has poor vision but good senses of hearing, smell and taste.
- It prefers cereals but will eat any food – feeding little and often.
- It does not need water as it is able to absorb enough water through eating moist foods.

A house mouse

How mice spread disease

Mice carry pathogenic bacteria, in particular salmonella and E. coli, in their gut and on their bodies. They contaminate food by:

- directly touching human food
- walking over food or work surfaces
- passing infected urine and faeces on to food and work surfaces.

Preventing mice from entering the premises

The best method of preventing mice from entering the premises is to practise good housekeeping:

- Seal all openings larger than ½ cm through which mice could enter. Ensure that there are no crevices or cracks in food cupboards. Plastic sheeting or screen, wood, rubber or other materials that can be gnawed are unsuitable for plugging holes used by mice.
- All places where food is stored, processed or used should be made mouse-proof.
- Dried grain and meat products should be stored in glass jars, metal canisters, re-sealable jars or other airtight containers.
- Doors, windows, and screens should fit tightly. It may be necessary to cover the edges with metal to prevent gnawing.

Rats

The most common rat in the UK is the brown rat. Rats are carriers of various pathogenic bacteria and are a major problem in urban areas. They are:

- usually brown with grey fur underneath
- about 200–270mm long plus a tail length of 150–200 mm
- live anywhere that provides food, water and shelter, for example in homes they will live in loft spaces, wall cavities, cellars or under floorboards; in gardens they will burrow into compost heaps and grassy banks or under sheds
- commonly found living in sewer systems
- prefer cereal products, although they will eat almost anything that humans eat
- breed frequently – one pair of rats will produce hundreds of offspring per year.

A brown rat eating from a waste bin

How rats spread disease

Rats can transmit many diseases to humans, including salmonella and Weils disease. They contaminate food by:

- eating from packets and waste bins
- fouling food with their urine and droppings
- walking over work surfaces and food storage areas
- contaminating food with their hairs and bodies.

Preventing rats from entering the premises

The best method of preventing rats from entering the premises is to practise good housekeeping:

- Remove potential nesting sites by keeping yards and gardens clean and tidy, and by cutting back overgrown areas.
- Do not feed wild birds or other animals to excess – you may be feeding rats as well.
- Keep the building in good repair so that rats cannot enter. Seal holes around pipes and gratings.
- Ensure that the drain inspection covers are in place and are in good repair.
- Do not leave household waste where rats can get at it.

How to recognise a rodent infestation

It is usually easy to spot if mice or rats have entered a building. Look out for the following tell-tale signs:

- Droppings. Common rat droppings are approximately 12 mm long and taper at both ends; mouse droppings are smaller.
- Fresh gnawing damage to food, food containers, wires and other materials.
- Nesting sites. Mouse nests, made from fine shredded paper or other fibrous material, are often found in sheltered spots.
- A strong urine smell. An infestation of rodents in any space within the house or building will be accompanied by quite a strong urine smell, especially if they've been there for some time.
- Damage in the form of chewed articles in cupboards and chewed insulation on the wiring in the roof space.
- Smear marks. These are greasy marks made from contact with rodent fur and are found particularly around holes, along skirting boards and around doors.
- Rat runs in the garden. These will show up as runs along the edges through the vegetation, as rats usually use the same pathways.

Dealing with rodent infestation

Mice and rats are very difficult to get rid of because they are adaptable, agile and breed rapidly. Your local authority will provide a service for the treatment of rats in domestic properties. Fully trained pest control officers will survey the infestation then place poison bait in the most appropriate locations, and make follow-up visits to ensure the treatment has been successful. Remember it is a legal requirement to report an infestation of rats or mice to your local authority.

Birds

Wild birds are not normally considered a pest in our gardens, but some have been found to carry pathogenic bacteria including salmonella and campylobacter. They include pigeons, starlings, magpies and sparrows.

How birds spread disease

If birds get into the food area they can:

- contaminate food and equipment with their droppings, feathers, and so on
- spread disease from the insects they carry on their bodies
- damage packaging in food storage areas.

Birds, especially magpies, have been known to contaminate milk by pecking through the foil tops of bottles which have been delivered to the door.

Preventing birds from entering food premises

The best method of preventing birds from entering the food area is to practise good housekeeping:

- Clean all spillages immediately.
- Rubbish bins should have close fitting lids.
- Ensure all openings are protected. Doors should be self-closing and plastic strips fitted to doors which are used regularly.
- Make sure there are no perches available to birds (for example gutters).
- Provide a covered area for milk bottles, if appropriate.

Dealing with a bird problem

Birds can be difficult to remove once they have gained access to a building. Any method of removal must comply with the Wildlife and Countryside Act 1981 which protects species and only allows humane methods of removal to be used.

Complying with the law

The food industry has a duty to keep its premises free from pests. For more information see Chapter 11.

Knowledge Test

1 Which of the following statements *best* defines a food pest?

  a A dead creature capable of contaminating premises either directly or indirectly.

  b Any creature that causes damage to buildings when entering.

  c A living creature capable of contaminating food either directly or indirectly.

  d Any creature that causes people to become ill due to eating them.

2 What should you do if a bird has pecked the top of your milk bottle? Give reasons for your answer.

(Answers on page 181.)

Chapter 11

Laws concerning food hygiene and safety

Caring establishments such as nursing homes, residential care homes, hospitals, day nurseries and schools are bound by law to ensure that the food they prepare and serve is safe to eat. As part of your responsibilities as a care practitioner, you will need to know how the laws and regulations relating to food hygiene and safety affect the way you work. They will apply to you whenever you prepare or serve food to clients.

This chapter looks at food safety legislation and safe working practices in food businesses and premises. These cover any food handling that you might do in the course of your work. This chapter addresses the following topics:

- **Food handlers – your responsibilities.**
- **Employers and the law.**
- **Safe working practices.**
- **The role of environmental health officers.**
- **First aid materials for food handlers.**
- **Your role in reporting food hazards.**

Food handlers – your responsibilities

When handling food you will be expected to maintain a high standard of **personal hygiene**, and the way in which you work must also be clean and hygienic. As a food handler you have a legal responsibility to safeguard food. The extent of your responsibility will depend upon the type of work you do and your role within the workplace.

Keys to Good Practice: Rules for food handlers

- ✔ Wear clean clothing and, where appropriate, protective clothing such as gloves and aprons.
- ✔ Follow good personal hygiene.
- ✔ Regularly wash your hands when handling food.
- ✔ Never smoke in food handling areas.
- ✔ Keep the workplace clean.
- ✔ Don't bring outdoor clothing into food areas.
- ✔ Report any illness (like infected wounds, skin infections, diarrhoea or vomiting) to your supervisor or manager immediately.
- ✔ You must not work with food if you have food poisoning or similar symptoms until your employer or doctor says it is safe to do so.
- ✔ Protect food and ingredients against contamination which is likely to make them unfit to eat or a health hazard. For example, uncooked poultry should not contaminate ready-to-eat foods, either through direct contact or through work surfaces or equipment.
- ✔ Don't sell food that is unfit for human consumption.
- ✔ Don't sell food which is beyond its sell-by date.
- ✔ Report any faults, problems or possible food hazards to your manager.

Employers and the law

There are four key food safety laws and regulations in Britain:

- the Food Safety Act 1990
- Food Premises (Registration) Regulations 1991
- Food Safety (General Food Hygiene) Regulations 1995
- Food Safety (Temperature Control) Regulations 1995.

Similar laws apply in Northern Ireland.

In addition to these four food safety laws and regulations, some food businesses, mainly manufacturers, will need to follow product-specific regulations.

Nursing homes and residential care homes in particular need to be aware of the Food Safety Act 1990 and the Food Safety (General Food Hygiene) Regulations 1995 as these apply to the safety of food being provided within the home.

In food businesses, food handlers must be given adequate supervision, instruction and/or training in food hygiene. Each food business must decide what training or supervision their food handlers need by identifying the areas of their work most likely to affect food hygiene.

The Food Safety Act 1990

Under this Act, employers must not:

- sell (or keep for sale) food that is unfit for people to eat
- cause food to be dangerous to health
- sell food that is not what the customer is entitled to expect, in terms of content or quality
- describe or present food in a way that is false or misleading.

Food that is 'unfit' to eat is not of a high enough standard for people to eat. It might be rotten (putrid) or poisonous (toxic). Food, particularly meat, will sometimes be marked 'unfit for human consumption' and it is an offence to sell such food to consumers. Food might become unfit if, for example, you keep it past its use-by date or do not prepare it correctly.

It is important that your employer takes positive steps to ensure good food hygiene. Usually this means putting a food safety system in place such as HACCP (see page 163). If you were prosecuted under the Food Safety Act, you would need to convince the court that you had taken all reasonable steps to avoid the offence of which you had been accused – this is called a **due diligence** defence.

Food Premises (Registration) Regulations 1991

Anyone planning to start a new food business will need to register with the local environmental health department 28 days before opening. If the owner changes the activity at the food premises, they must tell the local Environmental Health Department within 28 days of the change.

The Food Safety (General Food Hygiene) Regulations 1995

These regulations set out the basic hygiene principles that food businesses must follow in relation to staff, premises and food handling. Anyone who owns, manages or works in a food business – apart from those working in primary food production (such as harvesting, slaughtering or milking) – is affected by these regulations. They apply to anything from a hot dog van to a five-star restaurant, from a village hall where food is prepared to a large supermarket or vending machine. This is true whether you sell food publicly or privately, in a hotel or in a marquee, for profit or for fund-raising. The regulations do not apply to food cooked at home for private consumption.

The regulations require food businesses to:

- make sure food is supplied or sold in a hygienic way
- identify potential food **hazards**
- decide which of these hazards need to be controlled to ensure food safety
- put into place effective control and monitoring procedures to prevent the hazards causing harm to consumers.

Food safety management controls do not have to be complex, especially in small food businesses. However, refridgerators must be in place and routinely checked.

Food Safety (Temperature Control) Regulations 1995

These regulations cover:

- the stages of the food chain that are subject to temperature control
- the temperatures at which certain foods must be kept

- which foods are excluded from specific temperature controls
- when the temperature controls allow flexibility.

The regulations require that certain foods are kept at or below 8°C. They recommend that fridges should be kept at a temperature of between 2°C and 5°C. To make sure your fridge is at the right temperature, you will need to check it regularly using a fridge thermometer. There are no set temperatures for freezers although it is recommended that they operate at –18°C or below.

In Scotland the regulations apply but slightly differently. A maximum temperature for chilling foods is given, but businesses are still required to chill foods to keep them safe. Maximum times for keeping foods out of temperature controls for service or display are also not given. When reheated, foods must reach a minimum temperature of 82°C (180°F).

Safe working practices

In order to comply with food laws, food businesses must have systems in place that will ensure food is stored, prepared and cooked in a clean, safe and hygienic environment.

As mentioned above, the Food Safety (General Food Hygiene) Regulations 1995 requires owners of food businesses to identify potential food hazards and ensure that controls and monitoring procedures are put in place to protect consumers from the risk of food poisoning.

Ways to minimise food hazards include:

- maintenance of premises and equipment
- keeping foods at the right temperature
- control of food pests
- maintaining a clean environment
- stock control
- staff training
- illness exclusion
- using an effective safety system – HACCP.

Maintenance of premises and equipment

The Food Safety (General Food Hygiene) Regulations 1995 require that food premises and equipment must be maintained in good repair and condition.

- Regular maintenance reduces the risk of direct contamination of food during storage, preparation and cooking, for example from flaking wall plaster or rust from corroded equipment.
- Smooth, sound surfaces are easier to clean than damaged ones, so cleaning and disinfection will be improved.
- Equipment that is regularly maintained is less likely to become faulty or break down, and may last longer. Faulty equipment could cause a food hazard, for example a fridge operating at 10°C might allow pathogenic bacteria to grow. The regulations therefore help to ensure that equipment operates effectively and safely.

Scheduled maintenance checks

Checking the condition of premises and equipment should be done to a strict schedule. Using a schedule will:

- ensure that both equipment and structure are checked regularly
- help to identify hazards which can then be controlled.

Keeping written records

Written records can be used to:

- show that equipment has been serviced regularly – this could be important if a food business was trying to establish a defence in legal cases where, for example, a loose nut or bolt from a food mixer had found its way into a food product
- show that measures are in place to control food safety hazards
- identify areas and equipment that require regular maintenance
- provide a checklist to help ensure things are not missed.

Keeping foods at the right temperature

It is important that all foods are stored at the correct temperature and for the correct length of time as this will help to reduce the risk of food poisoning. Proper temperature control is a very important measure in preventing food poisoning and therefore must be strictly controlled. Food businesses should have a temperature control policy which involves staff keeping regular records of fridge and freezer temperatures. Records should:

- show food is being stored at temperatures which limit the growth of pathogenic bacteria
- provide a check that refrigerated equipment is working correctly.

While not a legal requirement, keeping records is important because they show that measures are in place to limit a major food safety hazard.

Control of food pests

Food pests are a potential hazard to food safety and hygiene. As you saw in Chapter 10, they carry bacteria which can lead to food poisoning if they come into contact with food. Pests can cause damage (rats and mice can gnaw through cables, pipes, food containers, and so on) and contamination can lead to quantities of food being thrown away.

Recording pest control methods

Although keeping records about identification and control of food pests is not a legal requirement, they are important in:

- establishing a defence in cases where, for example, insects have found their way into food which has then been sold, or where rodents have contaminated food with harmful bacteria
- showing that measures are in place to control a major food safety hazard.

The law states that:

- it is an offence to sell food which is unfit, substandard or which may cause harm to the person eating it
- food must be protected against contamination from pests.

Maintaining a clean environment

A basic requirement of food safety law is that food premises and equipment are kept clean. Failure to do so may result in legal action being taken against the owner of the business.

Thorough cleaning will help to prevent contamination of food by bacteria, foreign objects and chemicals. It will remove food debris and dirt on which food poisoning bacteria grow and gets rid of anything that may provide a food source or home for pests such as insects and rodents.

Dirt may also cause damage to equipment or mean that it operates less efficiently resulting in increased running and maintenance costs.

Food businesses may maintain a clean environment through the use of a cleaning schedule (see Chapter 9, pages 128–9). A schedule will provide a checklist to help ensure that things are not missed. It also makes it clear to staff what their cleaning duties are and what cleaning materials are safe and/or appropriate.

Stock control

Good stock control will help to avoid potential food safety hazards and prevent the food business from serving unfit food to its clients.

The law states that it is an offence to sell food which is 'unfit, injurious to health or contaminated in such a way that it would be unreasonable to expect it to be consumed in that state'. It is also an offence to sell or use food after the use-by date, even if the food appears to be all right.

First in first out

Rotating stock so that older stock is always stored in front of newer stock will ensure that you use food before its use-by or best-before date. It is an offence to sell or use food beyond the use-by date even if the food looks wholesome. Having to throw away food because it has passed its use-by or best-before date is also a waste of money.

It is bad practice to sell food after the best-before date. This is a guideline issued by the manufacturer in an effort to stop food businesses selling substandard food. If food was found to be unfit having being sold after its best-before date, this could be damaging to any **due diligence** defence.

Keeping stock control records

Although not required by law, stock control records might help:

- where it is necessary to establish a defence in cases where, for example, the history of the food needs to be traced
- to show that measures are in place to control food safety hazards
- in the investigation of any food complaint, by allowing the history of the food to be traced (for example where did it come from, what condition was it in, how old was it, what was the 'shelf life', when was it used?).

Methods of stock control

Below are some of the most commonly used stock control methods:

- Check all purchases/deliveries to confirm that the quality is acceptable and that all products are within date. Foods which arrive in damaged packaging may have been contaminated by foreign bodies, pests or micro-organisms.
- If products are transferred to larger or other storage containers, the containers should be labelled to show the contents and the date of arrival or the date by which they should be used. All containers should be closeable to prevent infestation by pests or accidental contamination by foreign bodies or micro-organisms.
- Packaged food products should be kept off the floor and away from walls, with adequate space between stock to enable regular inspection for pests and cleaning.
- Raw foods and cooked foods should be kept apart during storage. In fridges and freezers, cooked foods should be stored above raw food.

Staff training

Food handlers need to be trained to avoid potential food safety hazards:

- Mistakes when handling food can cause food poisoning which may lead to serious illness and even death.
- Not knowing hygiene rules can cost money. It can lead to claims for compensation from dissatisfied customers, unnecessary

wastage of food due to spoilage and fines resulting from legal action where hygiene laws are broken or substandard food has been sold. In some cases it can even lead to the closure of food businesses.

The Food Safety (General Food Hygiene) Regulations 1995 require owners of food businesses to ensure that food handlers are supervised and instructed and/or trained in food hygiene matters. The level of training given depends on the type of work the food handler is required to do.

Keeping records of training details

Written records are not a legal requirement but they will show that the food business has measures in place to ensure that staff know:

- how to recognise food safety hazards
- how to control any hazards to prevent things going wrong.

Where someone is accused of committing an offence under the Food Safety Act 1990, the main defence available to them is one of **due diligence**. Keeping training records would help to establish a defence in cases where the provision of appropriate training was an issue.

Illness exclusion

It is important that you do not handle food when you are ill as you may bring harmful bacteria into the workplace and contaminate the food. Under the Food Safety (General Food Hygiene) Regulations 1995 anyone working in a food handling area should report to their supervisor or manager if they are suffering from gastro-intestinal illnesses (see page 162). As long as you are not infectious, it is normally quite safe for you carry out your other duties. However, you must inform your employer of your illness as some employers insist that food handlers supply a negative stool specimen prior to their return to work.

You may return to work if you have been free of symptoms for at least 48 hours and are not taking any anti-diarrhoeal medicines – this does not include antibiotics – providing you are very thorough in your personal hygiene.

Keeping records of staff illness

While written records are not a legal requirement, they would be very useful in:

- trying to establish a defence in cases where exclusion of staff who were ill was an issue
- showing that measures are in place to ensure staff recognise the importance of leaving a food area when ill in order to prevent contamination.

Reporting illness

You must tell your employer or supervisor if you have had or are suffering from a **food-borne illness**, any illness with similar symptoms or if you have any condition which may cause food to become contaminated. Symptoms to report are:

- diarrhoea and/or vomiting
- nausea
- ear, eye or nose discharge
- infected wounds, sores or skin infections which leave an open wound or broken skin.

It is the employer's duty to ensure that staff know which illnesses to report.

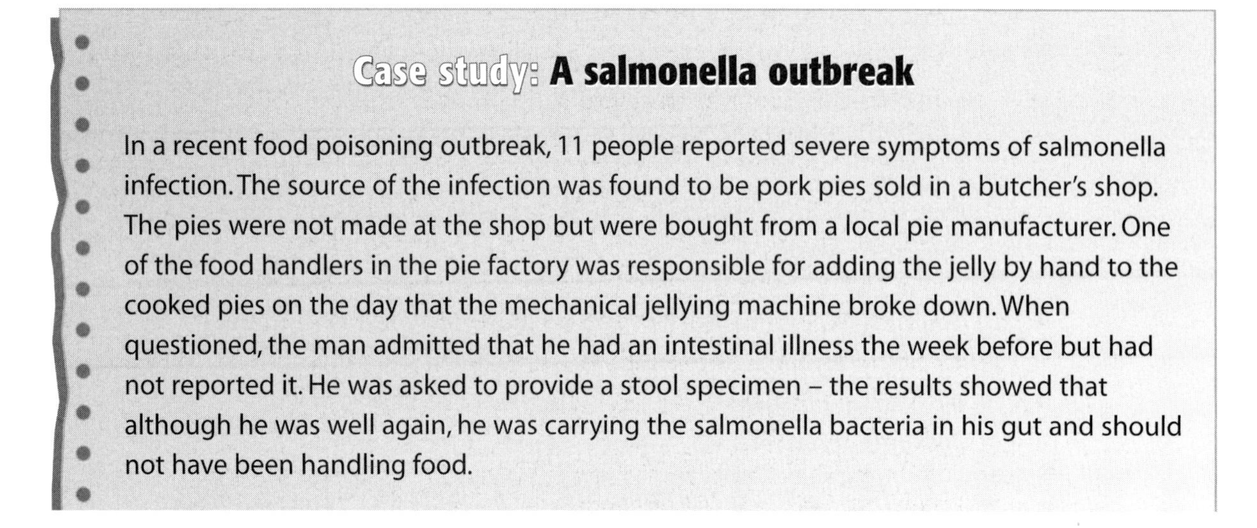

Case study: A salmonella outbreak

In a recent food poisoning outbreak, 11 people reported severe symptoms of salmonella infection. The source of the infection was found to be pork pies sold in a butcher's shop. The pies were not made at the shop but were bought from a local pie manufacturer. One of the food handlers in the pie factory was responsible for adding the jelly by hand to the cooked pies on the day that the mechanical jellying machine broke down. When questioned, the man admitted that he had an intestinal illness the week before but had not reported it. He was asked to provide a stool specimen – the results showed that although he was well again, he was carrying the salmonella bacteria in his gut and should not have been handling food.

Case study: A salmonella outbreak

Questions

1 Describe the symptoms of a salmonella infection.

2 What should the food handler in the case study have done?

3 What are the responsibilities of the food handler's employer?

Using an effective food safety system – HACCP

HACCP is a universal food safety system. HACCP stands for:

Hazard
Analysis
Critical
Control
Points

HACCP was designed to protect American astronauts from getting food poisoning on the first manned flights into space. It is now the most widely used food safety system in the UK.

HACCP aims to protect food from contamination by:

- Hazard analysis: identifying the **critical points** in the food handling process with regard to food safety
- Controls: putting in place controls to prevent microbiological, chemical and physical hazards from contaminating food
- Monitoring (checking controls): monitoring these points to make sure that contamination does not occur.

In a food premises HACCP involves identifying all the potential **hazards** at each stage in food handling from purchasing and delivery through to storage and preparation and finally to cooking and serving (see page 164). By writing the hazards down and identifying how to deal with them, an environmental health officer will be able to see that you have taken the right steps to protect your clients and reduce the likelihood of food poisoning.

Look at the hazard flow chart for pre-cooked meat on page 164 and the blank sample hazard flow chart on page 165.

Hazard Flow Chart for *Pre-cooked meat*

Stage	Hazards *What can go wrong?*	Controls *How can I prevent it going wrong?*	Monitoring *How can I check my control?*	Corrective action *What do I do if things are not right?*
Purchase/ delivery	Contamination from dirt inside vehicle or contact with raw foods.	Buy from a reputable source.	Audit supplier if possible. Check condition and packaging on delivery.	Reject deliveries which do not meet standards.
	Growth of food poisoning bacteria during delivery.	Insist on refrigerated deliveries (below 8°C).	Check temperatures on delivery.	
		Specify proper date marking of meat.	Check meat is within date code.	
Storage	Growth of bacteria already present.	Store at temperatures below 8°C.	Check fridge temperatures.	Adjust fridge where necessary.
		Ensure proper stock control (a first in first out system).	Weekly stock checks.	Review purchasing.
	Further contamination by bacteria.	Keep fridge clean.	Cleaning schedules.	Review: - frequency - products used - staff training.
		Separate from raw foods e.g. raw meat.	Visual checks. Staff supervision.	Staff training.
Preparation	Growth of bacteria already present.	Where possible prepare in cool area.	Check with a thermometer.	Ensure adequate ventilation.
				Reduce preparation time.
		Keep preparation time to a minimum.	Visual checks. Staff supervision.	Staff training.

Identifying and dealing with potential hazards in pre-cooked meat

Hazard Flow Chart for ______

Stage	Hazards *What can go wrong?*	Controls *How can I prevent it going wrong?*	Monitoring *How can I check my control?*	Corrective action *What do I do if things are not right?*
Delivery				
↓ Storage				
↓ Preparation				
↓ Cooking				
↓ Serving				

A sample hazard flow chart

To complete a hazard flow chart you will need to work through each of the following stages.

1 Identifying each stage	Identify each stage in the food handling process. These will vary depending on the food. Examples include: ❑ delivery (of ingredients) ❑ storage ❑ preparation ❑ cooling ❑ freezing ❑ defrosting ❑ reheating ❑ cold service ❑ hot service ❑ transport (to the client).
2 Complete the first stage	Fill in the first stage in the left-hand column of the hazard flow chart. In the pre-cooked meat flow chart this is purchase/delivery.
3 Identifying hazards	Identify the potential hazards for this stage (purchase/delivery) and write them in the second column. Such hazards will include things such as: ❑ growth of bacteria already present in the food ❑ contamination of the food from dirt inside the vehicle.
4 Controls	The next column asks you to identify the controls which you can put in place to prevent the potential hazards in column 2 from occurring. These might include: ❑ specifying acceptable delivery temperatures ❑ the proper use of date stamps ❑ using reputable suppliers, and so on.
5 Monitoring	In the column headed *Monitoring* write down the method by which you can check your controls are working or being followed. For purchase/delivery this might be: ❑ Refrigerated deliveries should arrive at 8°C or below. Checking the temperature of refrigerated goods on delivery will show whether or not the controls are being followed.
6 Corrective action	The last column is where you should put the action to be taken if monitoring reveals that control measures are not being followed.
7 Complete the hazard flow chart	Repeat the above steps for each of the remaining stages – storage, preparation, and so on. Look at the completed hazard flow chart for pre-cooked meat for further examples of hazards, controls, monitoring and corrective action.
8 Review	At regular intervals, review your system to ensure that changes to staff, equipment and legislation have been taken into account.
9 Informing staff	Finally, all staff need to be aware of the system and what their individual responsibilities are in relation to their tasks.

Keys to Good Practice: Food safety practices

Keeping food at the right temperature:

- ✔ Check the temperature of incoming food items.
- ✔ Ensure temperature gauges in cold rooms and fridges are set correctly.
- ✔ Store fresh items at or below 5°C and frozen food at or below –18°C.
- ✔ Rotate stock on a 'first in first out' basis.
- ✔ Check the temperature of fridges and freezers twice a day.
- ✔ Cook food to the right temperature – use a food thermometer if necessary.
- ✔ Check hot and cold holding temperatures every two hours.
- ✔ Hold hot food at or above 63°C and cold food at or below 8°C.

Prevent contamination:

- ✔ Wash raw fruit and vegetables.
- ✔ Store raw and cooked food separately.
- ✔ Use separate utensils and equipment for raw and cooked foods.
- ✔ Use single-use cloths instead of tea-towels or fabric cloths.
- ✔ Use colour-coded cloths, buckets and mops for different cleaning tasks.
- ✔ Follow hygienic procedures when working with food.

Follow personal hygiene procedures:

- ✔ Wash hands using an anti-bacterial soap and single-use paper towels – both before and during food handling.
- ✔ Report illnesses and do not work with food when sick.
- ✔ Wear the right uniform or appropriate protective clothing.
- ✔ Check that 'How to wash your hands' charts and stickers appear above hand wash basins. (Hand basins should contain no-touch taps and no-touch soap dispensers.)

Keep the workplace clean:

- ✔ Keep the work area and equipment clean.
- ✔ Use a disinfectant where appropriate.
- ✔ Follow a cleaning schedule (see Chapter 9, pages 128–9).

Control food pests:

- ✔ Keep pests out.
- ✔ Report all pest sightings.
- ✔ In the event of an infestation, use a professional pest control contractor.

The role of environmental health officers

Environmental health officers (EHOs) are responsible for ensuring that we live and work in a healthy and safe environment. One of their tasks is to check the safety of food at all stages of production from storage to distribution. This involves:

- visiting food premises and advising managers on hygiene and safety
- running courses to educate food handlers and trying to raise consumer awareness of how to prevent food poisoning in the home
- ensuring that food premises and food handlers follow laws and regulations relating to food safety
- inspecting premises to see that health standards are maintained
- investigating possible offences
- checking to see if food is safe – they have the power to take away suspect food
- taking companies and individuals to court if they break any of the food safety laws.

EHOs may visit a range of settings throughout the local authority area including shops, factories and offices. Some of the visits may be to dirty and sometimes potentially dangerous places and may be unpleasant. Officers will wear protective clothing hats, masks, boots and overalls as and when required, for example during visits to premises such as abattoirs and food preparation factories. EHOs are required to appear at court to give evidence from time to time.

Sunshine Nursery
44 Park Road
Anytown
AB1 2CD

19 May 2003

Dear Parent

As you may be aware, two children in the nursery school have developed salmonella infection. This germ can cause a mild form of gastro-enteritis with diarrhoea, fever, nausea, headache, abdominal pain and vomiting. Sometimes a more serious illness can result, especially in very young babies, small children and elderly people. The germ is usually spread in food which has been contaminated with salmonella, but can be spread person-to-person by direct contact with the infected faeces, hence the importance of hand washing after using the toilet.

The local Control of Infection Unit and Environmental Health Department is investigating the outbreak. They have advised that children who develop these symptoms should remain at home until 48 hours after the diarrhoea has stopped. Your general practitioner will provide any necessary treatment. The school has been advised about other appropriate local control measures and these are currently being implemented.

Please read the enclosed fact sheet which contains information about the illness.

Yours sincerely

Barbara Hudson
Nursery Manager

Guidance letter for parents at a nursery school

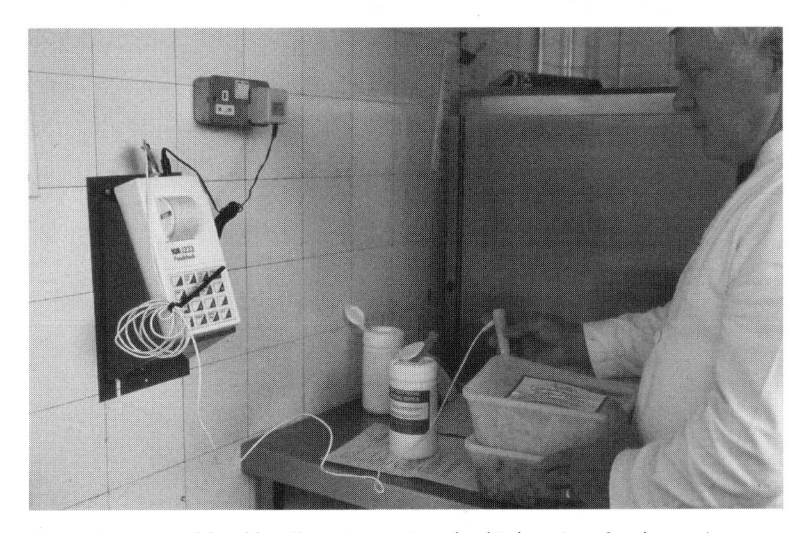

An environmental health officer inspecting the kitchen in a food premises

First aid materials for food handlers

All food businesses and other places which involves staff in regular food handling must have a first aid kit which contains the following items:

- sterile washproof plasters (blue)
- sterile eye pads
- triangular bandages
- safety pins
- medium dressings
- large dressings
- moist wipes
- latex gloves (blue)
- fingerstalls (blue)
- cooljel sachet
- plaster strapping (blue).

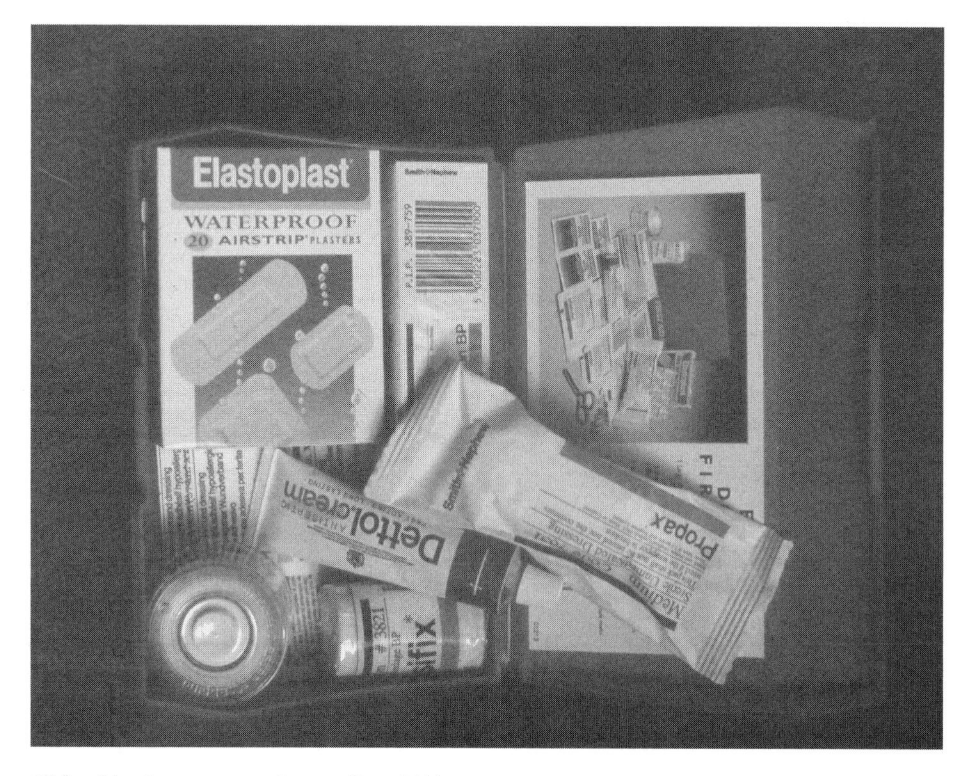

All food businesses must have a first aid kit

Your role in reporting food hazards

If your workplace has an outbreak of gastro-intestinal infection, a number of general measures will need to be undertaken immediately to limit further spread. These should be put in place after calling the Control of Infection Unit and the Environmental Health Department and include those outlined below.

Keys to Good Practice: Dealing with a food poisoning outbreak

- ✔ Ensure that everyone realises the importance of thorough hand washing – this must be carried out after going to the toilet and before eating food.
- ✔ Disposable paper towels must be used for hand drying by both children or clients *and* carers.
- ✔ Review both the systems of hygiene and food preparation procedures. The local Environmental Health Department will undertake a catering inspection if appropriate.
- ✔ Affected food handlers must seek advice from their local EHO before returning to work.
- ✔ Children and carers with diarrhoea and/or vomiting should stay at home until clear of symptoms for at least 48 hours. (There are recommended exclusion periods for specific diseases.)
- ✔ Additional environmental cleaning and disinfection may be required as advised by the Control of Infection Unit.
- ✔ In a children's nursery, routine activities such as cookery and sand or water play may need to be suspended for the duration of the outbreak – the Control of Infection Unit can give advice.
- ✔ More specific control activities will depend on the course of the outbreak and will be advised by the Control of Infection Unit.

Activity: Hazard Analysis

The Food Safety (General Food Hygiene) Regulations 1995 require food businesses to undertake a 'hazard analysis' as part of the management of food safety.

1 Describe what a hazard analysis is.

2 Outline the advantages to a food business of carrying out a hazard analysis exercise.

3 Briefly outline the steps involved in a hazard analysis exercise for a food business. Using examples, explain how the depth and detail of the exercise depends upon the nature of the business involved.

Knowledge Test

Choose the right answer in each case.

1 What does the food safety system HACCP stand for?
- a Hazard Analysis Catering Control Plan
- b Hazard Analysis Critical Control Point
- c Hazard Awareness Crisis Control Pointers

2 What is the place where a hazard can be removed or reduced known as?
- a Crisis control point
- b Cryogenic control place
- c Critical control point

3 Which of the following is the single most important aspect of HACCP?
- a It helps produce good quality foods.
- b It prevents hazards occurring.
- c It assists businesses to comply with food legislation.

4 What is a food hazard?
- a Anything which could make food unsafe to eat.
- b Anything which means a food business could be taken to court.
- c Anything which makes food less value for money.

(Answers on page 181.)

Glossary

Ambient temperature The temperature of the surrounding environment, usually meaning ordinary room temperature.

Antibiotics Drugs used to treat infections caused by bacteria.

Assymptomatic infection An infection without any symptoms.

Bacteria A group of micro-organisms. Most are harmless, but a few cause illness such as food poisoning.

Best-before date A date on food packaging that indicates when food should be eaten to be in its best condition.

Binary fission The way in which bacteria multiply – by growing and dividing into two.

Carrier A person who carries food-poisoning bacteria without having its symptoms.

Cleaning The removal of dirt and grease.

Contaminant Any substance or object which makes food harmful or unwholesome.

Contamination The presence in food of pathogenic micro-organisms or foreign objects.

Core temperature The temperature at the centre or thickest part of the food.

Critical points Points at which food safety hazards can be controlled.

Cross contamination The transfer of harmful bacteria from one food to another. Harmful bacteria can not only be transferred from food to food, but also from hands to food, breathing on food and from animal contact.

Dehydration The removal of moisture; drying.

Dementia A general decline in all areas of mental ability.

Detergent A substance used to remove dirt during cleaning (does not kill micro-organisms).

Due diligence A legal defence where you must prove that you had taken all reasonable steps to avoid the offence of which you have been accused.

Environmental health officer (EHO) A local or national government employee whose role is to enforce food safety legislation in Britain.

Food hygiene All the practical measures involved in keeping food safe and wholesome through all the stages of production to sale or consumption.

Food pests Rodents, birds and insects which live on and in food for human consumption.

Food poisoning An illness caused by eating food contaminated by harmful substances or by harmful micro-organisms living on the food.

Food-borne illness Any illness, such as food poisoning, which is caused by contaminated food.

Freezer burn Appears as greyish-brown leathery spots on frozen food. It occurs when air reaches the food's surface and dries out the product. Although undesirable, freezer burn does not make the food unsafe.

Gastro-enteritis An inflammation of the stomach and intestinal tract (gut) that normally results in diarrhoea.

Hazard Analysis Critical Control Point (HACCP) A system for ensuring food safety through the identification, assessment and control of hazards in the food chain.

Halal A diet followed by Muslims in which meat is killed in a particular way before it is eaten.

Hazard Something which has the potential to lead to food poisoning, for example the presence of pathogens in raw meat.

High risk foods Foods which are particularly likely to develop food poisoning bacteria.

Incubation period The time it takes for the symptoms of a food-borne illness to start after contaminated food has been eaten.

Immunodeficiency A lowering of the body's ability to fight off infection and disease.

Immuno-suppression The use of drugs or techniques to suppress or interfere with the body's immune system and its ability to fight infections and disease.

Mould Fungus which occurs on the surface of foods such as fruit and stale bread.

Pasteurisation A form of heat treatment which kills pathogenic bacteria but not all spoilage bacteria.

Parasite An animal or plant living in or on another living organism and feeding on it.

Parkinson's disease A condition which affects the nervous system, causing the individual to have poor balance, mobility and posture and often causing the hands to shake uncontrollably.

Pathogen An organism which causes disease.

Perishable Food which spoils quickly.

Personal hygiene The way a person maintains their health, appearance and cleanliness.

pH The pH scale is used to measure the strength of acids and bases (or alkalis). Neutral is pH 7 (that is, neither acidic or alkaline). The acid strength in the human stomach is about pH 2. Caustic soda and basic household cleaners have a pH of about 12–14.

Preservation The safe treatment of food to delay spoilage.

Ready-to-eat foods Foods which are not prepared or treated immediately before eating in a way that would kill pathogenic bacteria.

Spoilage The effect of certain types of moulds, yeasts or bacteria which causes food to 'go off' or decay, making it unacceptable to eat.

Spores A protective coating formed by some bacteria which enables them to survive in difficult conditions, for example in low temperatures.

Sterilisation The process of killing all pathogenic micro-organisms in food.

Stroke Also called Cerebral Vascular Accident (CVA), this is when blood supply to part of the brain is damaged, often resulting in paralysis on one side of the body and difficulties in swallowing.

Symptomatic infection Infection with symptoms (for example vomiting, headache).

Temperature danger zone The range of temperatures at which most bacteria multiply – above 8°C and below 63°C.

Toxins Poisons produced by some bacteria, for example when they multiply in food.

Use-by date A date on food packaging displayed on highly perishable foods that indicates when the food is safe to eat.

Viruses Micro-organisms which are smaller than bacteria.

Yeasts Fungi which is used in a controlled way to ferment beer, wine, cider and soy sauce as well as in making bread, flavouring agents and Marmite™.

Useful addresses

Food Standards Agency
Aviation House
125 Kingsway
London
WC2B 6NH
Tel: 020 7276 8000
Web: www.food.gov.uk
E-mail: helpline@foodstandards.gsi.gov.uk

Food Standards Agency Scotland
St Magnus House
6th Floor
25 Guild Street
Aberdeen
AB11 6NJ
Tel: 01224 285100

Food Standards Agency Wales
1st Floor
Southgate House
Wood Street
Cardiff
CF10 1EW
Tel: 029 2067 8999

Food Standards Agency Northern Ireland
10C Clarendon Road
Belfast
BT1 3BG
Tel: 02890 417711

Websites

Food Standards Agency	www.foodstandardsagency.gov.uk
Foodlink	www.foodlink.org.uk
Control of substances hazardous to health	www.hse.gov.uk/coshh
British Pest Control Association	www.bpca.org.uk
Caterer	www.caterer.com

Chapter 1: The importance of food hygiene

Knowledge Test, page 13:

1 Babies and young children; elderly people and people who are already ill (they have a reduced immunity).

2 Antacids create an alkaline medium in the stomach, encouraging the growth of bacteria.

Chapter 2: Microbiology

Knowledge Test, page 25: **1d**; **2e**; **3h**; **4f**; **5g**; **6c**; **7a**; **8b**

Chapter 3: The causes of food poisoning

Knowledge Test, page 46:

1b Some bacteria can produce dangerous toxins which are not destroyed even by thorough cooking. Remember also that cooked food can become contaminated if it comes into contact with an unwashed utensil, dish, work surface or hand that was used to prepare tainted uncooked food.

2d Food poisoning is most likely to strike from two hours to two days after eating. But some toxins in fish work within minutes, while botulism could take up to a week.

3b Stomach acid helps to destroy bacteria, so people who regularly take antacids are more likely to get food poisoning than people who only take them occasionally or not at all.

4a It does not take many salmonella to make you ill. The ice cream that made almost one quarter of a million people ill in the USA in 1994 contained about *six* salmonella bacteria in each serving.

5d Although minced beef is the most common source of E. coli food poisoning, apples and lettuce that are contaminated with animal manure have also been linked to outbreaks.

6b Salmonella and campylobacter cause 80 per cent of all food poisoning illnesses (and 75 per cent of all deaths) from contaminated meat and poultry. Most of the damage comes from poultry.

7a

Chapter 4: Contamination and cross contamination

Knowledge Test, page 58:

1f Roughly one out of every 10,000 eggs is contaminated with salmonella bacteria; these eggs may not be cracked, dirty or unrefrigerated. If the ovaries of the hen that laid an egg were contaminated, salmonella could have got into the egg before its shell formed. That is why all raw eggs should be handled as if they *were* contaminated and should be cooked thoroughly.

2e Bloody diarrhoea or pus in the stool is the classic sign of an E. coli infection. Headache, stiff neck *and* a fever may be a sign of listeria infection. Continuous diarrhoea could lead to life-threatening dehydration. Weakness, numbness or tingling could be a sign of botulism or food poisoning from contaminated seafood.

3b You cannot taste, see or smell pathogens which cause food poisoning. They do not change the taste, appearance or smell of foods.

Chapter 5: Maintaining good personal hygiene

Knowledge Test, page 69:

1c

2 Any four of the following:

- ❑ Hand contamination from infected cuts.
- ❑ Re-use of unwashed tasting spoons.

- ❑ Coughing or sneezing directly on to food.
- ❑ Coughing or sneezing causing hand contamination.
- ❑ Hand contamination due to poor hand washing after visiting toilet.
- ❑ Contamination of food/hand contact surfaces.

3a or c

4b Staphylococcus aureus tends to come from cuts, wounds or boils.

Chapter 6: Principles of safe storage

Activity, page 89:

1 False. Refrigeration slows but does not prevent the growth of harmful bacteria. Always remember to refrigerate food quickly.

2 True.

3 False. Although food takes longer to defrost, always defrost food in the fridge – this is the safest method for all foods. Use the microwave to defrost food only if it will then be cooked immediately.

4 False. Do not overfill the fridge. Cold air must be able to circulate inside the fridge to keep food cold and safe. Tidy the fridge regularly.

5 True. Thermometers are important kitchen tools. Regularly check the temperature of the fridge using a fridge/freezer themometer.

6 False. Perishables, prepared food and leftovers need to be refrigerated or frozen within two hours of purchase or preparation. If the room temperature is above 0°C, foods should not be left out for longer than an hour.

7 True.

8 True.

9 False. Travel with the cool bag stored in the coolest part of the car. The boot is usually one of the hottest spots because of lack of ventilation.

Knowledge Test, page 90–1:

1a You can be sure of the quality if you eat food by its best-before date.

2c Perishable foods must be stored correctly and thrown away if past the use-by date.

3c A use-by date must have a specific day on it.

4c If you fail to store a food properly, it may not be safe to eat.

5a Date marks help to prevent food poisoning by making sure food is not kept for too long.

6b Fresh chilled ready-to-eat meals must be eaten by a certain date, so they must display a use-by date label.

7b The stock is rotated by putting the newest stock at the back of the fridge or store cupboard and the oldest at the front.

8c

9b

10a Milk that has reached its expiry date is still safe and nutritious and will probably not go sour for another week or so.

Chapter 7: Food preparation and cooking

Knowledge Test, pages 106–7:

1c In particular, high risk foods include ready-to-eat foods which are not going to be cooked again before they are eaten.

2a

3c Sliced ham is unlikely to be cooked or heated again before it is eaten.

4c You should always defrost food thoroughly in the fridge to make sure it never gets too warm.

5b The instructions on the label will give you the most precise information about how to cook the meal.

6b Not cooking food properly can mean that bacteria are left in the food and could even be allowed to multiply.

7a The other examples are unlikely to be food poisoning. Rice is a rich breeding ground for bacteria.

8e Options a–d are signs of food spoilage. You generally cannot see any signs of food poisoning bacteria in food.

Chapter 9: Cleaning and disinfecting food areas

Knowledge Test, page 138: **1b**; **2c**; **3c**; **4b**

Chapter 10: Control of pests in the workplace

Knowledge Test, page 151:

1c

2 Discard the milk – it may be contaminated with salmonella or campylobacter bacteria and so could cause food poisoning.

Chapter 11: Laws concerning food hygiene and safety

Knowledge Test, page 172: **1b**; **2c**; **3b**; **4a**

Index